The Ultimate Visual Guide

Animal Kingdom

WINDMILL
BOOKS

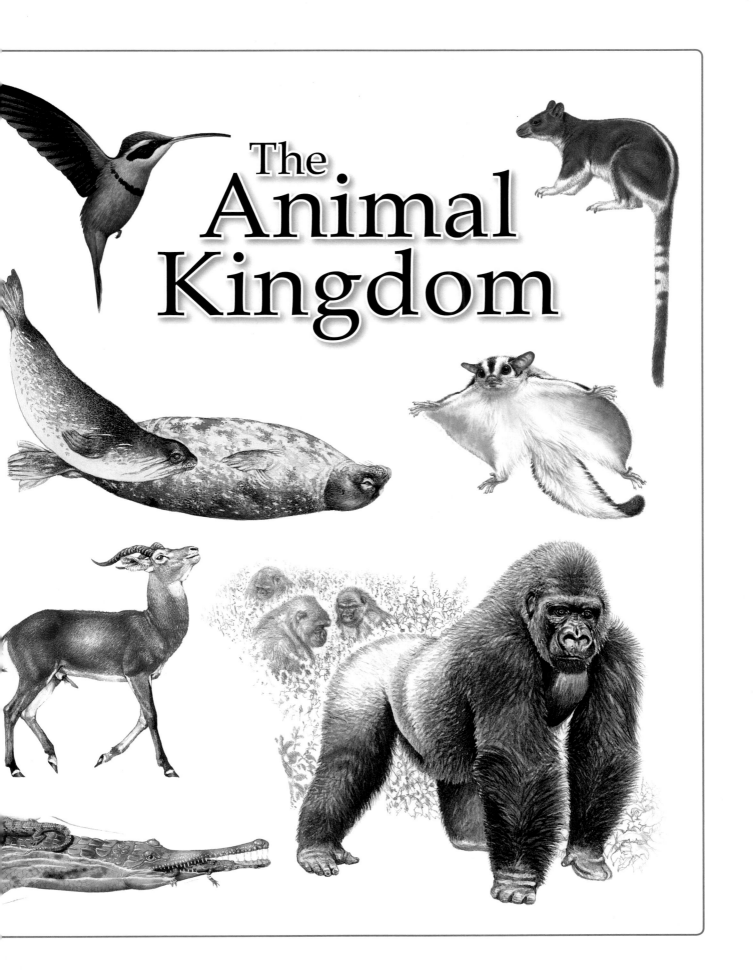

The
Animal
Kingdom

CONTENTS

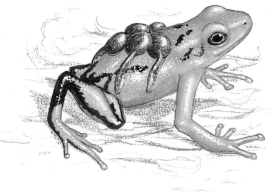

WHAT IS AN AMPHIBIAN?

WHAT IS A REPTILE?

WHAT IS A FISH?

WHAT IS AN INSECT?

INTRODUCTION

People have long marveled at the seemingly endless variety of form shown within the animal kingdom, from giant whales plunging the ocean depths to tiny birds that fly thousands of miles over mountains and deserts without stopping. Behavior is equally diverse, ranging from bats that use echolocation to detect and catch tiny insects at night to fish attracting prey with bioluminescent lures. This book looks at the animal kingdom in all its glory. It is divided into sections organized by animal class—mammals, birds, amphibians, reptiles, and insects, and a short section on spiders. An introductory spread defines the characteristics of each class, and each section is further

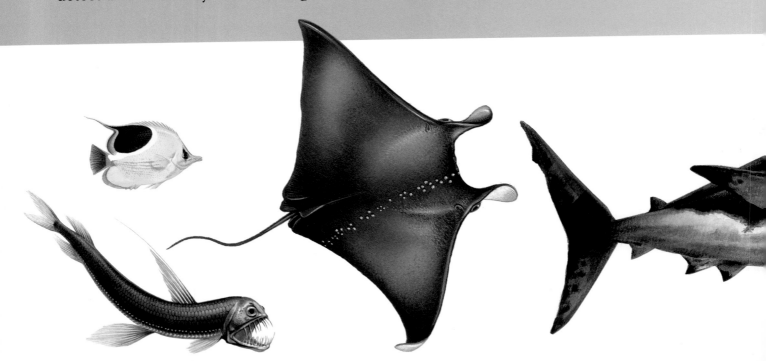

divided into spreads devoted to a family or group of related families.

Each page is packed with amazingly detailed artworks, many of which show the animals in their natural habitat and behaving as they would in the wild. An orangutan is shown swinging from a branch, a bird-of-paradise is illustrated during a courtship display, and hyenas are depicted in pursuit of zebra prey. Captions describe something of each animal's range, habitat, behavior, food, or hunting technique, while annotations highlight key features of their anatomy.

With over 900 artworks, this book really is the *Ultimate Visual Guide to the Animal Kingdom*.

WHAT IS A MAMMAL?

Mammals are endothermic (warm-blooded) vertebrates. This means their bodies are covered by hair and they nurse their young with milk. They also exhibit an extraordinary range of form, function, and behavior: most are terrestrial, but many are largely aquatic or hunt mostly on the wing. Most of the 5,000-plus mammals are placental, but there are also marsupials and the monotremes lay eggs.

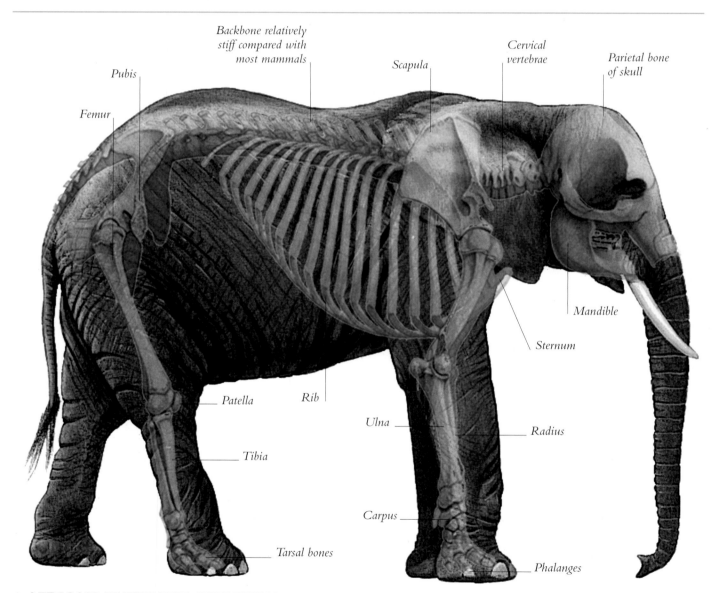

Backbone relatively stiff compared with most mammals

Pubis

Femur

Scapula

Cervical vertebrae

Parietal bone of skull

Mandible

Sternum

Patella

Rib

Ulna

Radius

Tibia

Carpus

Tarsal bones

Phalanges

▲ AFRICAN ELEPHANT SKELETON

All mammals have a skeleton that can be divided into three major sections: the skull, the backbone and ribs, and the limb bones. All the main elements of a mammal's skeleton can be seen in the African Elephant, though this is a particularly massive mammal.

▶ A CARNIVORE'S JAW

The massive temporalis muscle of a carnivore's jaw delivers the power to suffocate or crunch through bone. The masseter muscle provides the force needed to cut and grind flesh.

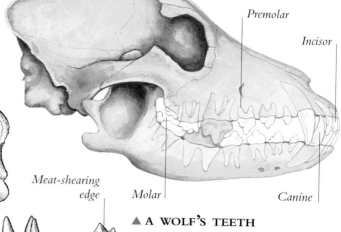

Premolar

Incisor

Temporalis muscle applies force here

Molar

Canine

Meat-shearing edge

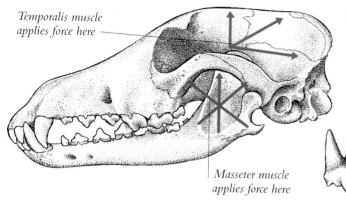

Masseter muscle applies force here

▲ A WOLF'S TEETH

A wolf has three incisors, one canine, four premolars, and three molars on each side of its lower jaw.

▼ HINDGUT FERMENTERS AND RUMINANTS

Ungulates (hoofed mammals) have evolved two different systems for dealing with cellulose in fibrous plant food: hindgut fermentation and rumination.

Hindgut fermenters: cell contents are completely digested in the stomach, then pass to the cecum and large intestine, where the cellulose of the plant cell walls is fermented by microorganisms.

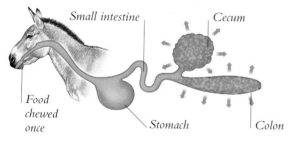

Small intestine

Cecum

Food chewed once

Stomach

Colon

Ruminants: food passes to the rumen. It is then regurgitated. Rechewing regulates particle size, with smaller particles passing through the reticulum and omasum to the true stomach (abomasum), where digestion is completed.

Absorption of fermentaion products

Fermentation of cellulose sugars

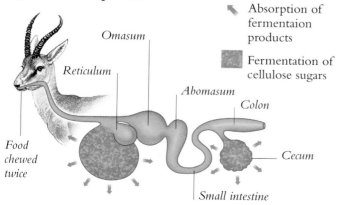

Omasum

Reticulum

Abomasum

Colon

Food chewed twice

Cecum

Small intestine

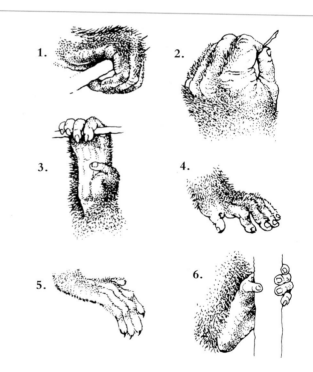

1.   2.

3.   4.

5.   6.

▲ PRIMATE HANDS AND FEET

Hand and foot dexterity is more developed among the primates than any other group of animals.
1. Spider monkey: much-reduced thumb of hand for arm-swinging. **2. Gorilla:** thumb opposable to other digits allows precision grip. **3. Gibbon:** short opposable thumb well distant from arm-swinging grip of fingers. **4. Macaque:** short opposable thumb in hand adapted for walking. **5. Tamarin:** long-foot of branch-running species. **6. Orangutan:** broad foot with long grasping big toe for climbing.

MARSUPIALS

Unlike placental mammals, marsupials are born at a very early stage of development. They continue to grow in the pouch of the mother. Kangaroos and wombats usually give birth to single young, but pygmy possums have litters of up to four. Marsupials live in Australasia and the Americas and range in size from large kangaroos to tiny planigales.

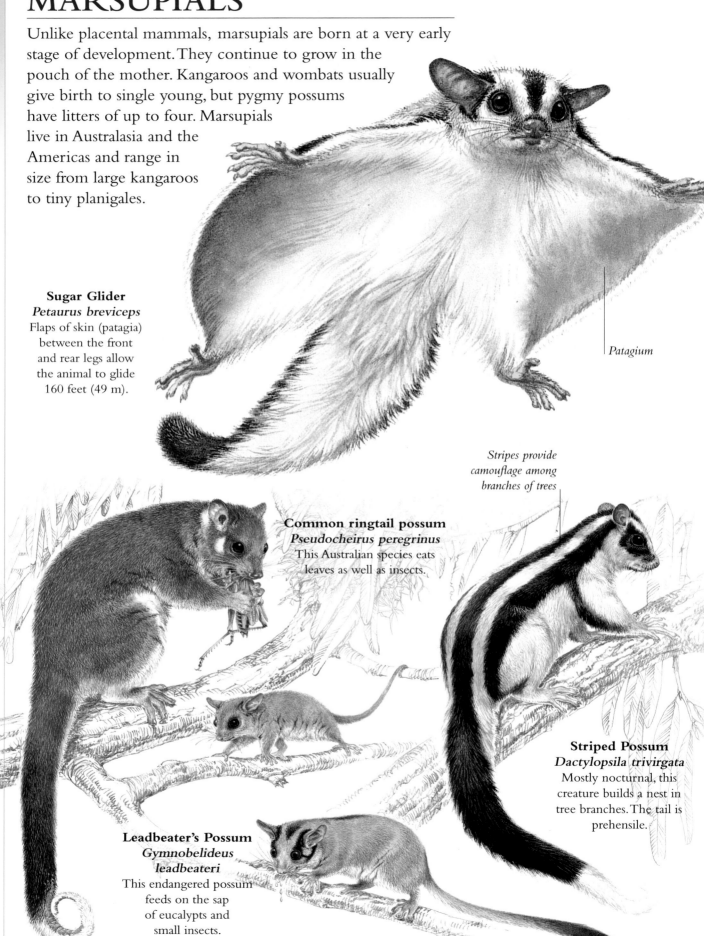

Sugar Glider
Petaurus breviceps
Flaps of skin (patagia) between the front and rear legs allow the animal to glide 160 feet (49 m).

Patagium

Stripes provide camouflage among branches of trees

Common ringtail possum
Pseudocheirus peregrinus
This Australian species eats leaves as well as insects.

Striped Possum
Dactylopsila trivirgata
Mostly nocturnal, this creature builds a nest in tree branches. The tail is prehensile.

Leadbeater's Possum
Gymnobelideus leadbeateri
This endangered possum feeds on the sap of eucalypts and small insects.

Derby's Woolly Opossum
Caluromys derbianus
Living in Central American rain
forests, this species eats nectar,
insects, leaves, and seeds.

Black-shouldered Opossum
Caluromysiops irrupta
An important pollinator of South
American trees, this opossum
moves from plant to plant in
search of nectar.

Gray Four-eyed Opossum
Philander opossum
The sharply defined white spot
above each eye is distinctive,
hence this animal's name.

Mexican Mouse Opossum
Marmosa mexicana
This small species has a prehensile
tail almost as long as its body.

Common Brushtail Possum
Trichosurus vulpecula
Perhaps Australia's most widespread
marsupial, this nocturnal creature
even inhabits cities.

Scaly-tailed Possum
Wyulda squamicaudata
This solitary nocturnal
forager feeds on leaves,
flowers, and fruit.

Water Opossum
Chironectes minimus
At home in rivers and
lakes, this web-footed
New World species hunts
frogs and fish.

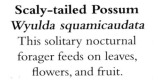

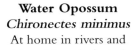

Webbed hind toes

KANGAROOS

Kangaroos and wallabies (family Macropodidae, known as macropods) live in Australia and New Guinea. Some live on open grassland but others inhabit forests and are good climbers. There are 76 species, and all have long tails, prominent ears, and strong hind legs that enable them to bound at up to 43 miles per hour (69 km/h).

Joey in pouch

Common Wallaroo
Macropus robustus
Living in some of the driest parts of Australia, wallaroos can survive for up to three months without drinking; all the water they need comes from their food.

Proserpine Rock Wallaby
Petrogale persephone
The 16 species of rock-wallabies are nocturnal feeders, and this species is the most endangered of them.

Red Kangaroo
Macropus rufus
This is the world's largest kangaroo. The female's gestation period is 6–7 weeks before the joey is born and moves to her pouch.

Pretty-faced Wallaby
Macropus parryi
This social marsupial sometimes
forms mobs of 50 animals.

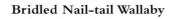

Red-legged Pademelon
Thylogale stigmatica
There are seven species of pademelons,
small macropods that feed on fruits,
berries, and leaves on rain forest floors or
on open grassland near forest.

Bridled Nail-tail Wallaby
Onychogalea fraenata
This shy, solitary animal has a
population of little more than 1,000.

Yellow-footed Rock Wallaby
Petrogale xanthopus
This species has a very limited
range in Australia. The banded tail
is very distinctive.

Burrowing Bettong
Bettongia lesueur
Sheltering in burrows during the day,
these bettongs become active at night.

Goodfellow's Tree Kangaroo
Dendrolagus goodfellowi
Agile in the forest trees of New
Guinea, this creature has been
known to leap 30 feet (9 m) to the
ground without ill-effect.

Quokka
Setonix brachyurus
This relative of the kangaroos can climb
trees in search of leaves. It has a very
restricted range in Western Australia.

*Black bands
on back*

Banded Hare Wallaby
Lagostrophus fasciatus
Inhabiting just two islands off the coast of Western
Australia, this small wallaby is now an endangered species.

ELEPHANTS AND RHINOS

Elephants are the largest land mammals still in existence.
They live for as long as humans, are able to learn and remember,
and are sometimes used as working animals. Together they make
up the family Elephantidae. Rhinoceroses, like elephants and
hippopotamuses, are megaherbivores, a category of mammals that
was once much more diverse. There are five species of rhinos
(family Rhinocerotidae), two in Africa and three in Asia.

Asian Elephant
Elephas maximus
Slightly smaller than its African
cousins, the Asian species has
obviously smaller ears.

Savanna Elephant
Loxodonta africana
The largest land mammal on Earth
weighs up to 14,000 pounds (6.3 tonnes)
and is distinguished by its large ears.

Evolution of the elephants
From left to right, **Moeritherium** (Oligocene),
Trilophodon (mid-Miocene), **Platybelodon** (late
Miocene), **Imperial Mammoth**, *Mammuthus
imperator* (Pleistocene), and **Savanna Elephant**,
Loxodonta africana (modern).

*Giant
curved tusk*

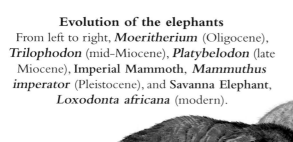

Indian Rhinoceros
Rhinoceros unicornis
This single-horned species is Asia's second-largest land mammal, after the Asian Elephant.

Javan Rhinoceros
Rhinoceros sondaicus
This is now probably the rarest large mammal on Earth, with just one population living in the wild.

Sumatran Rhinoceros
Dicerorhinus sumatrensis
Habitat loss in its native Sumatra and Borneo is a threat to this species' survival.

Black Rhinoceros
Diceros bicornis
Males are 10–12 years old before they form a territory and mate. Their slow reproductive cycle has held back the recovery of their numbers in Africa.

White Rhinoceros
Ceratotherium simum
The largest of the rhinoceros species, the biggest recorded male weighed more than 9,900 pounds (4.5 tonnes).

ANTEATERS, SLOTHS, AND ARMADILLOS

The four species of anteaters (family Myrmecophagidae) live in the New World and feed exclusively on insects. They are sometimes grouped with sloths (two families) and armadillos (Dasypodidae) as edentates. The 21 species of armadillos also live in the Americas. They have a tough protective carapace, or shell, and can roll up into a ball when threatened. Like anteaters and sloths, armadillos eat insects.

Nine-banded Armadillo
Dasypus novemcinctus
The most widespread of the armadillos, this species eats ants, termites, and other invertebrates.

Long snout probes for insects

Prehensile tail

Southern Tamandua
Tamandua tetradactyla
This solitary South American species breaks open insects' nests with its strong claws.

ARMORED SHELLS

All armadillos have armored shells, but their form differs from species to species. Compare that of the Southern Three-banded Armadillo (below), with the Pichi (bottom), whose shell is completely banded.

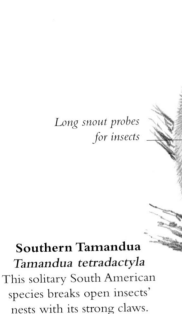

Three bands

Shell composed entirely of bands

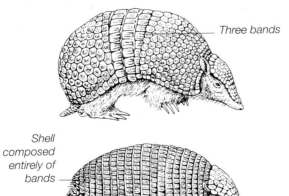

Giant Ground Sloth
Megatherium
This extinct ancestor of
modern sloths lived in
South America and grew to
20 feet (6 m) long.

Prehistoric edentates
From left to right, the giant anteater
Scelidotherium, which lived in South
America in the Pleistocene; the shelled
Pleistocene edentate *Glyptodon panochthus*;
and the tiny armored pangolin *Eomanis
waldi*, which lived in Germany in the Eocene.

SQUIRRELS

Among the most widespread of mammals, squirrels (family Sciuridae) live in habitats ranging from tropical rain forests to tundra, and from alpine meadows to city parks. Some species nest in cavities in trees, while others dig underground burrows. Squirrels are mostly herbivores, but invertebrates feature in their diet and many will also take birds' eggs and nestlings. There are almost 300 species, many of which hibernate.

Asiatic Chipmunk
Tamias sibiricus
In many parts of this mammal's range several individuals will share a burrow in which to hibernate through the cold winter months.

Patagium between front and hind limbs

Southern Flying Squirrel
Glaucomys volans
This resident of the eastern forests of the United States glides—rather than flies—from tree to tree.

Alpine Marmot
Marmota marmota
This mountain species is a habitual burrower, capable of digging into even the hardest ground.

Prevost's Squirrel
Callosciurus prevostii
A beautifully colored forest species, this squirrel lives in Southeast Asia.

Abert's Squirrel
Sciurus aberti
Ponderosa pines in the Rocky
Mountains are the preferred
habitat for this species.

Indian Giant Squirrel
Ratufa indica
This large squirrel grows to
more than 3 feet (90 cm) long.

*Black stripe between
flanks and belly*

Shrew-faced Ground Squirrel
Rhinosciurus laticaudatus
This squirrel lives in Southeast
Asia. It is also known as the
Long-nosed Squirrel.

American Red Squirrel
Tamiasciurus hudsonicus
Buds and seeds, especially those in
the cones of conifers, make up most
of the American Red Squirrel's diet.

Geoffroy's Ground Squirrel
Xerus erythropus
Habitats ranging from swamp forest
to cultivated land provide a home
for this species in its native Africa.

NEW WORLD RATS AND MICE

There are more than 400 species in the subfamily Sigmodontinae. These rodents live in all terrestrial habitats, including tropical forests and savanna, cultivated land, temperate forest, and high-altitude plains. Most eat invertebrates and plant material, and some hunt small vertebrates, including fish. The largest species, South American Giant Water Rat, weighs up to 1.5 pounds (700 g).

Sumichrast's Vesper Rat, *Nyctomys sumichrasti* (above), is a nocturnal fruit-eater; it builds nests in trees.

Chiapan Climbing Rat, *Tylomys bullaris* (left), is also arboreal, rarely coming down from the tree canopy.

Wood rats, or pack rats
Neotoma species
These are nest-builders, using twigs and other debris. They are particularly fond of shiny objects, which they sometimes take from human habitation.

Cotton rats
Sigmodon species
Cotton rats are omnivores, living in the southern United States and northern South America. Unusually for a rat, young Hispid Cotton Rats are born fully furred.

Birds' eggs form part of cotton rats' diet

South American grass mice
Akodon species
Many grass mouse species live in a variety of South American habitats, from moist forest to semiarid country.

Mole mice
Chelemys species
Native to South America, three species of mole mouse live in underground burrows.

South American climbing mice
Rhipidomys species
These arboreal species live in primary and secondary forest in South America.

Pygmy mice
Baiomys species
This is the smallest rodent in the New World; it also has a tiny home range.

Fish-eating rats
Ichthyomis species
Predators of fish, crustaceans, and aquatic arthropods, fish-eating rats live in freshwater streams in South America.

White-footed Mouse
Peromyscus leucopus
Relatively common in eastern North America, this mouse is renowned for its jumping ability.

Swamp Rat
Scapteromys tumidus
This rat lives in flooded grass areas, where it nests beneath matted grass rather than burrows.

South American water rats
Nectomys species
These rodents are adapted for a life burrowing in moist environments, especially near rivers.

Leaf-eared mice
Phyllotis species
Most live at high altitudes, up to 14,300 feet (4,300 m) or more on the Andean plateau.

VOLES AND LEMMINGS

Most voles and lemmings (subfamily Arvicolinae) are herbivores, though Muskrats also eat mussels and snails. There are about 150 species in the group, and they occupy a wide range of habitats in North America and Eurasia. Burrowing species are common in tundra, temperate grasslands, steppe, and open forest. Aquatic or semiaquatic voles include the Muskrat and European Water Vole. Some species produce several litters every year.

Plant material makes up 95 per cent of a Muskrat's diet

Muskrat
Ondatra zibethicus
A hallmark of this semiaquatic species is its elaborate nest, built with an underwater entrance to give protection from predators.

Southern Mole Vole
Ellobius fuscocapillus
This is a burrowing vole of open steppe habitats in Iran, Afghanistan, and Pakistan. Some populations live at great altitudes.

Taiga Vole
Microtus xanthognathus
A common species of the North American taiga, females of this species give birth to litters of 6–13 young.

Arctic Lemming
Dicrostonyx torquatus
This individual is in its all-white winter coat, which makes the animal hard to see when it is on snow.

AGGRESSIVE LEMMINGS

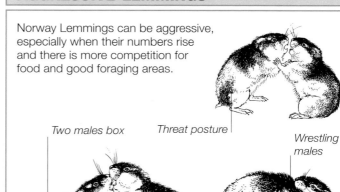

Norway Lemmings can be aggressive, especially when their numbers rise and there is more competition for food and good foraging areas.

Two males box *Threat posture* *Wrestling males*

Red Tree Vole
Arborimus longicaudus
It builds nests in the canopy of old-growth forests in the Pacific Northwest of North America.

Norway Lemming
Lemmus lemmus
During winter, lemmings live in insulated spaces beneath snow. Females are sexually mature at 3 weeks and can produce a new litter every 3–4 weeks.

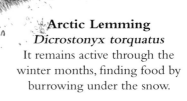

Arctic Lemming
Dicrostonyx torquatus
It remains active through the winter months, finding food by burrowing under the snow.

Meadow Vole
Microtus pennsylvanicus
Active by day and by night, this North American species creates a network of runways through vegetation.

European Water Vole
Arvicola terrestris
This species excavates burrows in river banks; it eats 80 per cent of its bodyweight every day.

OLD WORLD RATS AND MICE

Although a few species are endangered, the Old World rats and mice (subfamily Murinae) together form the most successful group of mammals on Earth. This, the largest subfamily of rodents, ranges across most parts of the Old World, occupying a great range of habitats. Most of the 542 (at least) species are terrestrial, but some are arboreal or semiaquatic. Rats and mice are famously fast breeders, with large broods and short gestation periods—lasting just 20–30 days for most small species.

Australian Water Rat
Hydromys chrysogaster
Australia's largest rodent hunts underwater for fish, amphibians, and aquatic insects.

Malabar Spiny Dormouse
Platacanthomys lasiurus
The hairs on this rodent's tail get longer toward the tip, giving it a graduated shape.

Greater Big-footed Mouse
Macrotarsomys ingens
This species' large feet are adaptations for living in the branches of trees in Madagascar.

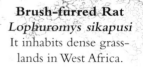

Brush-furred Rat
Lophuromys sikapusi
It inhabits dense grass-lands in West Africa.

Glandular patch

Crested Rat
Lophiomys imhausi
When this African species is agitated it raises its crest, exposing the glandular areas on the flanks. The hairs in this area are often smeared in poison from the bark of a tree—a deterrent for any would-be attacker.

Four-striped Grass Mouse
Rhabdomys pumilio
Females typically give birth to litters of five pups, which are sexually mature at 5–6 weeks. This mouse is an important part of the diet of southern African snakes.

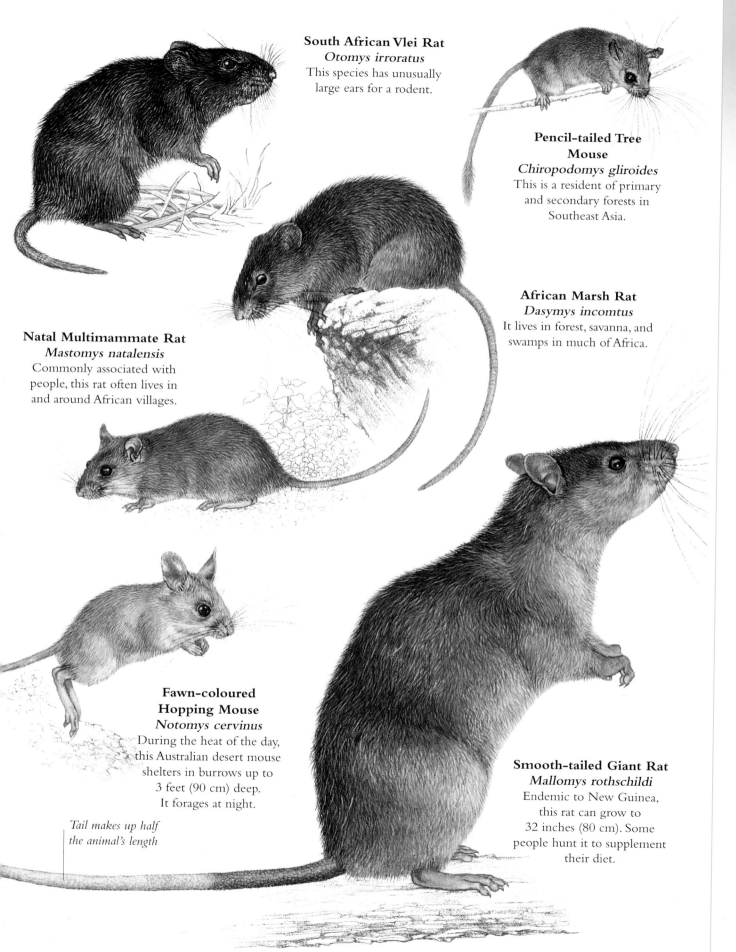

South African Vlei Rat
Otomys irroratus
This species has unusually
large ears for a rodent.

**Pencil-tailed Tree
Mouse**
Chiropodomys gliroides
This is a resident of primary
and secondary forests in
Southeast Asia.

Natal Multimammate Rat
Mastomys natalensis
Commonly associated with
people, this rat often lives in
and around African villages.

African Marsh Rat
Dasymys incomtus
It lives in forest, savanna, and
swamps in much of Africa.

**Fawn-coloured
Hopping Mouse**
Notomys cervinus
During the heat of the day,
this Australian desert mouse
shelters in burrows up to
3 feet (90 cm) deep.
It forages at night.

*Tail makes up half
the animal's length*

Smooth-tailed Giant Rat
Mallomys rothschildi
Endemic to New Guinea,
this rat can grow to
32 inches (80 cm). Some
people hunt it to supplement
their diet.

GERBILS AND GOPHERS

Gerbils are exclusively Old World rodents (subfamily
Gerbillinae), while pocket gophers form a New World family
(Geomyidae). Gerbils are adapted for life in arid and semiarid
environments, even the Sahara Desert. Most species are
nocturnal, spending the days in burrows. Pocket gophers
are named for their external, fur-lined pouches in both
cheeks, used for storing food.

This **Common Brush-tailed
Gerbil**, *Gerbillurus paeba* (above
right), of southern Africa, is grooming
its muzzle. **Tamarisk Jird**, *Meriones
tamariscus* (right), is a widespread and
abundant species in Central Asia.

Botta's Pocket Gopher
Thomomys bottae
Coloration in this species (above and
below) is very variable, with black, dark
brown, and even buff individuals.

Michoacan Pocket Gopher
Zygogeomys trichopus
This species (right) lives high in
the mountains of Mexico, where
habitat destruction is a problem.

*Food stored in hidden
pouches in each cheek*

Plains Pocket Gopher
Geomys bursarius
Solitary and territorial, this species
excavates burrow systems that are
hundreds of feet long.

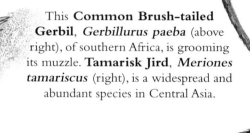

Short-eared Gerbil
Desmodillus auricularis
This southern African gerbil is
displaying submissive behavior by
crouching close to the ground.

Fat Sand Rat
Psammonys obesus
This North African desert
species has two litters a year.

Great Gerbil
Rhombomys opimus
The burrow system of the
Great Gerbil has separate
chambers for sleeping
and food storage.

Libyan Jird
Meriones libycus
Gerbils can be aggressive
when threatened. This jird
is launching an attack.

Mongolian Jird
Meriones unguiculatus
A female, with hair raised, darts
away from a male during its
ritualized mating behavior.

Lesser Egyptian Gerbil
Gerbillus gerbillus
By rubbing a gland on the desert sand,
this gerbil is leaving behind secretions
that will advertise its presence.

PORCUPINES, GUNDIS, AND ALLIES

Porcupines' arrays of spines offer them excellent protection from predators. The Old World porcupines (family Hystricidae) are terrestrial animals, while those of the New World (family Erethizontidae) spend much of their lives in trees. Gundis (family Ctenodactylidae) live in Africa, in deserts and on rocky mountainsides. They eat almost any plant they find, hiding from the sun in the hottest parts of the day. Cavies are South American rodents (family Cavidae) that occupy a range of habitats.

Some quills are nearly 1 foot (30 cm) long

Dassie Rat
Petromus typicus
A flattened skull and flexible ribs allow this rat to squeeze into crevices between rocks.

North African Crested Porcupine
Hystrix cristata
The crested porcupines of the Old World have stout, sharp, cylindrical quills around a short tail; if shaken, the quills produce a warning rattle.

Paca
Agouti paca
The only animal in the family Cuniculidae, this resident of South American forests has internal and external cheek pouches.

American spiny rats
Family Echimyidae
There are at least 80 species of these cavy-like rodents with flat, flexible spines or—less commonly—soft fur.

Paracana
Dinomys branickii
This is a rare, nocturnal creature of the western Amazon Basin.

Lesser Cane Rat
Thryonomys gregorianus
A herbivore living in marshes and along river banks, this species is widespread in sub-Saharan Africa.

Short-tailed Chinchilla
Chinchilla chinchilla
Hunted extensively for its fur in the past, protection is now allowing this endangered species to recover.

Chinchilla Rat
Abrocoma bennettii
This little creature is endemic to Chile.

Indonesian Porcupine
Thecurus **species**
The three members of this genus live on the islands of Borneo, Sumatra, and the Philippines.

Hutia
Family Capromyidae
Hutias have a robust body, relatively small eyes and ears, and short limbs. They inhabit Caribbean islands.

Gundis
Five species of gundis live in the deserts and mountains of north and northeast Africa. Right, from top to bottom: **North African Gundi**, *Ctenodactylus gundi*; **Mzab Gundi**, *Massoutiera mzabi*; **Felou Gundi**, *Felovia vae;* and **Speke's Gundi**, *Pectinator spekei.*

RABBITS AND HARES

The long-legged hares habitually use speed to escape predators, while rabbits have shorter legs and usually run for the cover of a burrow or dense vegetation. Together, they form the family Leporidae, the lagomorphs. Long ears are typical of all lagomorphs, with these being particularly magnificent in the jackrabbits. All rabbits and hares are herbivores, most feed at night, and some have very fast rates of reproduction.

Very long ears regulate body temperature

European Rabbit
Oryctolagus cuniculus
A burrow-living rabbit native to the Mediterranean region but introduced to many other parts of the world

Antelope Jackrabbit
Lepus alleni
This species survives in Mexican deserts by feeding on cacti.

Bunyoro Rabbit
Poelagus marjorita
This nocturnal lagomorph lives on damp grassland in Central Africa.

Natal Red Rockhare
Pronolagus crassicaudatus
The southern African rockhares occupy crevices in rocks during the day and feed at night.

Riverine Rabbit
Bunolagus monticularis
This is one of the world's rarest mammals. There are probably no more than 400—all in South Africa.

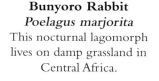

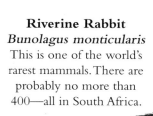

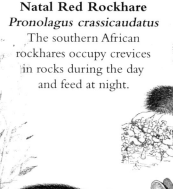

Amami Rabbit
Pentalagus furnessi
A forest-dwelling rabbit of the Amami Islands, Japan, this species excavates burrows and feeds by night.

Hispid Hare
Caprolagus hispidus
Inhabits Indian *sal* forest and
uses burrows excavated by
other animals.

Black-tailed Jackrabbit
Lepus californicus
This North American rabbit
hides and sleeps in small
shrubs, not burrows.

Eastern Cottontail
Sylvilagus floridanus
This is a common species in much
of North America and northern
South America.

Sumatran Striped Rabbit
Nesolagus netscheri
This rare lagomorph lives in
burrows in remote montane
forests in Sumatra, Indonesia.

European Hare
Lepus europaeus
It is renowned for its frenzied spring
activity, which includes "boxing"
between males and females.

Snowshoe Hare
Lepus americanus
In the northern parts of its
North American range, this
hare turns white in winter.

*Long limbs aid
quick running*

LEMURS AND BUSH BABIES

These groups of primates share a common ancestor. Living only in Madagascar, lemurs (family Lemuridae) and dwarf lemurs (family Cheirogaleidae) spend most of their time in trees, with some species restricted to humid forests and others to dry and spiny forests. Lemurs' diet includes fruits, flowers, leaves, and shoots. Bush babies (family Galagidae) and lorises and pottos (family Lorisidae) are all active by night. They live in Africa (but not on Madagascar) and South and Southeast Asia.

Ring-tailed Lemur
Lemur catta
This lemur lives in troops (groups) of up to 25 animals.

Black-and-white Ruffed Lemur
Lemur catta
The largest of all the lemurs, this species feeds in the forest canopy.

Brown Lemur
Eulemur fulvus
Some feed by day, others at night. The color of the coat is very variable.

Gray Bamboo Lemur
Hapalemur griseus
Lives in bamboo forests and reed beds.

Hairy-eared Dwarf Lemur
Allocebus trichotis
This endangered species has a diet of fruit, tree sap, and insects.

Bengal Slow Loris
Nycticebus bengalensis
An important seed disperser
and pollinator in Southeast
Asian forests

Thick-tailed Galago
Otolemur crassicaudatus
This bush baby eats birds, eggs,
small mammals, and reptiles in
southern African forests.

Gray Slender Loris
Loris lydekkerianus
This Asian species has a striking
face pattern and no tail.

Potto
Perodicticus potto
Large and muscular, the Potto feeds
mainly on fruits although bats, birds,
and rodents are sometimes taken.

Demidoff's Galago
Galagoides demidoff
A strictly arboreal species, this
bush baby builds complex
spherical leaf nests for sleeping.

Angwantibo
Arctocebus calabarensis
Caterpillars make up the biggest element
of this loris's diet. It prefers the forest
understory to the tree canopy.

NEW WORLD PRIMATES

New World primates have evolved into an extraordinary array of anatomical, social, and ecological types, many of them unique. The diverse primate families of South and Central America include capuchins and squirrel monkeys, night monkeys, titis and sakis, howler monkeys, spider monkeys, marmosets, and tamarins.

Large eyes assist night vision

Northern Night Monkey
Aotus trivergatus
This is the only truly nocturnal monkey, becoming active shortly after sunset.

Black Howler Monkey
Alouatta caraya
Howler monkeys are particularly vocal early in the morning when they join in a chorus of howling from high up in the trees.

Females have a pale buff coat

Marmosets and tamarins
1. **Goeldi's Monkey**, *Callimico goeldii*, Brazil, Bolivia, Peru, Colombia and Ecuador.
2. **Black-tailed Marmoset**, *Mico melanurus*, Brazil, Bolivia and Paraguay.
3. **Geoffroy's Tamarin**, *Saguinus geoffroyi*, Colombia, Panama and Costa Rica.
4. **Golden-headed Lion Tamarin**, *Leontopithecus chrysomelas,* Brazil.
5. **Santarém Marmoset**, *Mico humeralifer*, Brazil.
6. **Pygmy Marmoset**, *Cebuella pygmaea*, Colombia, Peru, Ecuador, Bolivia and Brazil.
7. **Red-bellied Tamarin**, *Saguinus labiatus*, Brazil, Bolivia and Peru.
8. **Saddle-back Tamarin**, *Saguinus fuscicollis*, Brazil, Bolivia, Peru and Ecuador.

TARSIERS AND TAMARINS

Tarsiers (family Tarsiidae) have the largest eyes of any mammals relative to their bodyweight. They live on the islands of Sumatra, Borneo, Sulawesi, and the Philippines. Tamarins (family Callitrichadae) are some of the most diverse and colorful primates of the New World. They occupy a range of forest types, from tall primary rain forest to the drier forests of northern Colombia and Central America.

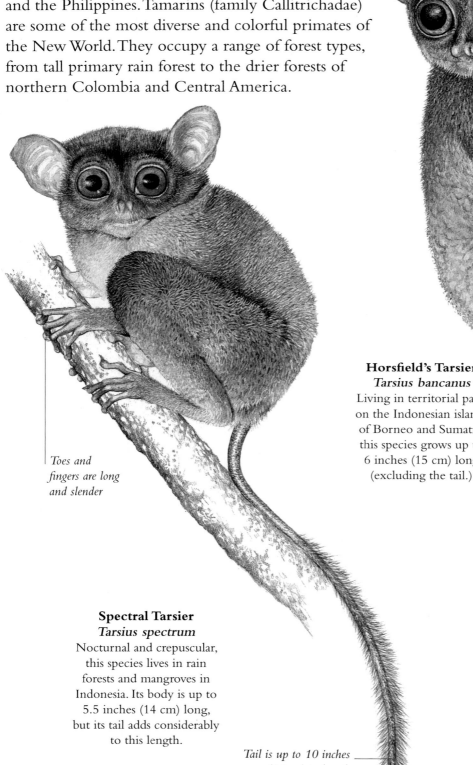

Toes and fingers are long and slender

Horsfield's Tarsier
Tarsius bancanus
Living in territorial pairs on the Indonesian islands of Borneo and Sumatra, this species grows up to 6 inches (15 cm) long (excluding the tail.)

Spectral Tarsier
Tarsius spectrum
Nocturnal and crepuscular, this species lives in rain forests and mangroves in Indonesia. Its body is up to 5.5 inches (14 cm) long, but its tail adds considerably to this length.

Tail is up to 10 inches (26 cm) in length

Cotton-top Tamarin
Saguinus oedipus
Older offspring delay their own breeding by staying within the
family unit and caring for younger siblings. In the family group
illustrated, a father (**1**) carries a very young infant on his back
while an older offspring (**2**) grooms the young tamarin. Another
young helper (**3**) receives the twin of the first infant (**4**) from its
mother (**5**), who has been suckling it.

GUENONS, BABOONS, AND MACAQUES

These Old World primates (subfamily Cercopithecinae) live in sub-Saharan Africa and South and Southeast Asia. Baboons, mangabeys, and macaques have bright patches of bare skin on the face and rump. The Gelada baboon also has a patch on the chest. Most species have only a limited mating season, and gestation lasts for 5–6 months. The diet is primarily fruit, but can also include bugs and small vertebrates.

Bonnet Macaque
Macaca radiata
This macaque occupies a variety of terrestrial and arboreal habitats.

Lip-smacking to bond with infant

Gelada
Theropithecus gelada
This primate lives on grasslands in Ethiopia. It has an area of naked pink flesh around the base of its neck.

Barbary Macaque
Macaca sylvanus
It lives in northern Algeria and Morocco, with a managed population in Gibraltar.

Mandrill (left) and Drill
Mandrillus sphinx and *M. leucophaeus*
An adult male Mandrill has a brightly colored blue and red face. The Drill's black face has a fringe of white fur around it.

Yellow Baboon
Papio cynocephalus
Individuals use at least ten different vocalizations to communicate with each other.

Long-tailed Macaque
Macaca fascicularis
A Southeast Asian species, this macaque's preferred habitat is rain forest.

Moor Macaque
Macaca maura
With a population in the low thousands and a distribution limited to the Indonesian island of Sulawesi, this species is now endangered.

Hamadryas Baboon
Papio hamadryas
This silver-gray baboon lives in rocky desert and semidesert, where it feeds on grass, seeds, and invertebrates.

Guinea Baboon
Papio papio
These baboons live in troops, usually 30–40 strong.

Olive Baboon
Papio anubis
Apart from a more pointed black nose and different colored fur, this species is similar to Hamadryas Baboon.

Chacma Baboon
Papio ursinus
One of the biggest baboons, adult males may grow to 45 inches (115 cm) long.

GIBBONS AND GREAT APES

Gibbons, or lesser apes (family Hylobatidae), live in the forests of Southeast Asia. The great apes (family Hominidae) comprise chimpanzees, gorillas, orangutans, and humans. All apes are intelligent and practice prolonged maternal care, ranging from 18 months in gibbons to three years or more in the great apes.

Kloss's Gibbon
Hylobates klossii
Females give birth to a single young every 2–3 years. The young gibbon is weaned in the middle of its second year but is not fully mature until the age of seven.

Dark cap is shared by both sexes

Silvery Javan Gibbon
Hylobates moloch
Active by day in undisturbed rain forest on the island of Java, females of this species are great songsters.

Common Chimpanzee
Pan troglodytes
Chimpanzees sometimes kill other animals, though most of their diet consists of plant matter. This chimp has killed a young antelope.

Sumatran Orangutan
Pongo abelii
Orangutans have suffered greatly as a result of forest clearance. The Sumatran species is critically endangered.

The silvery back shows this to be an adult male

Western Gorilla
Gorilla gorilla
This is the largest primate species and—after the chimpanzees—the closest relation of humans.

COLUGOS AND TREE SHREWS

There are just two species of colugos (family Cynocephalidae), gliding mammals of Southeast Asia, which are capable of traveling 230 feet (70 m) through the air, from tree to tree. Tree shrews (families Tupaiidae and Ptilocercidae) are neither shrews nor exclusively arboreal, with some species being entirely terrestrial.

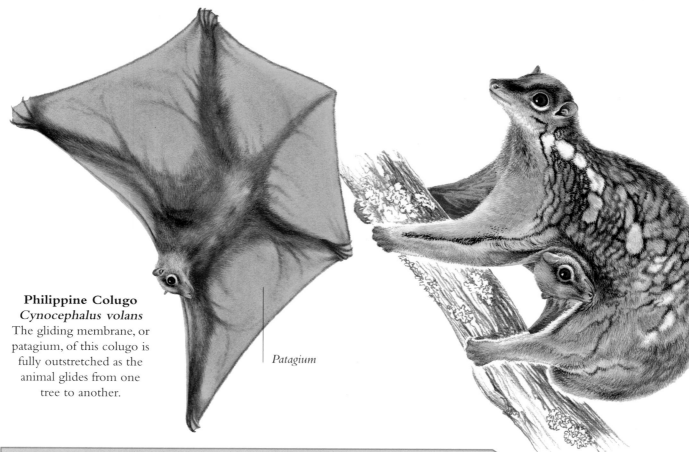

Philippine Colugo
Cynocephalus volans
The gliding membrane, or patagium, of this colugo is fully outstretched as the animal glides from one tree to another.

Patagium

Malayan Colugo
Cynocephalus variegatus
This female is carrying her young, which will not reach adulthood until it is 2–3 years old.

TREE SHREW SKULLS

Skulls are longest in those species that root around in leaf litter rather than feed in trees. Note also the relatively poorly developed canines and sharp-cusped molar teeth, typical of insectivorous mammals.

TERRESTRIAL OR ARBOREAL
1. **Mindanao Tree Shrew**, ground-dwelling
2. **Terrestrial Tree Shrew**, ground-dwelling
3. **Common Tree Shrew**, semi-arboreal
4. **Pygmy Tree Shrew**, arboreal

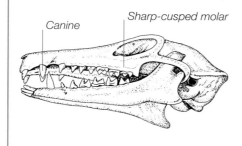

Canine

Sharp-cusped molar

1. 2. 3. 4.

A selection of tree shrews
(clockwise, from top left)
1. Pygmy Tree Shrew, *Tupaia minor:* Malay Peninsula, Sumatra, Borneo
2. Pen-tailed Tree Shrew, *Ptilocercus lowii:* Malay Peninsula, Sumatra, Borneo
3. Common Tree Shrew, *Tupaia glis:* Thailand, Malay Peninsula, Sumatra
4. Large Tree Shrew, *Tupaia tana:* Sumatra, Borneo
5. Mindanao Tree Shrew, *Urogale everetti:* Mindanao island, Philippines
6. Northern Smooth-tailed Tree Shrew, *Dendrogale murina:* Thailand, Laos,
Cambodia and Vietnam

HEDGEHOGS AND MOLES

Having spines means hedgehogs (family Erinaceinae) don't always need to run away from predators. Instead, they can roll up into a ball. Moonrats and gymnures (subfamily Galericinae) are their spineless near relatives. Although moles and desmans are in the same family (Talpidae), they have different lifestyles, with moles being diggers, and the two species of desmans being semiaquatic.

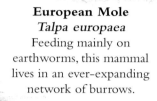

European Mole
Talpa europaea
Feeding mainly on earthworms, this mammal lives in an ever-expanding network of burrows.

Star-nosed Mole
Condylura cristata
Pink, fleshy appendages around the snout act as sensory organs for this swimming mole.

True's Shrew Mole
Dymecodon pilirostris
This species is endemic to Japan.

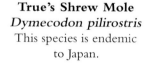

Pyrenean Desman
Galemys pyrenaicus
The fur is double-layered, with with a short, dense waterproof underfur and oily guard hairs.

American Shrew Mole
Neurotrichus gibbsii
This, the smallest American mole, burrows in deep, loose soils.

Hainan Gymnure
Neohylomys hainanensis
It is restricted to the island of Hainan, China, where it is very rare.

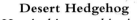

North African Hedgehog
Atelerix algirus
Up to 5,000 brown and white
spines cover this animal's body.

Desert Hedgehog
Hemiechinus aethiopicus
This mammal lives in North African
and Middle Eastern deserts. It
hibernates in January and February.

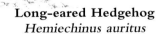

Shrew Gymnure
Hylomys sinensis
A strictly nocturnal burrowing species.

Short-tailed Gymnure
Hylomys suillus
Lives at altitudes up to
10,000 feet (3,050 m)
in Southeast Asia.

Long-eared Hedgehog
Hemiechinus auritus
This animal's large ears help it radiate
heat in the hot deserts where it lives.

Greater Moonrat
Echinosorex gymnura
Although related to
hedgehogs, moonrats
resemble rats.

Mindanao Moonrat
Podogymnura truei
Nocturnal and terrestrial, moonrats hide under
logs or in old burrows during the day.

BATS

The 18 families of bats form the order Chiroptera. They are remarkable creatures in many respects. Some can fly at 30 mph (50 km/h) in almost complete darkness, while their orientation systems allow them to fly through narrow gaps and catch tiny flying insects at night. Bats can survive cold weather by hibernating, virtually shutting down their body systems.

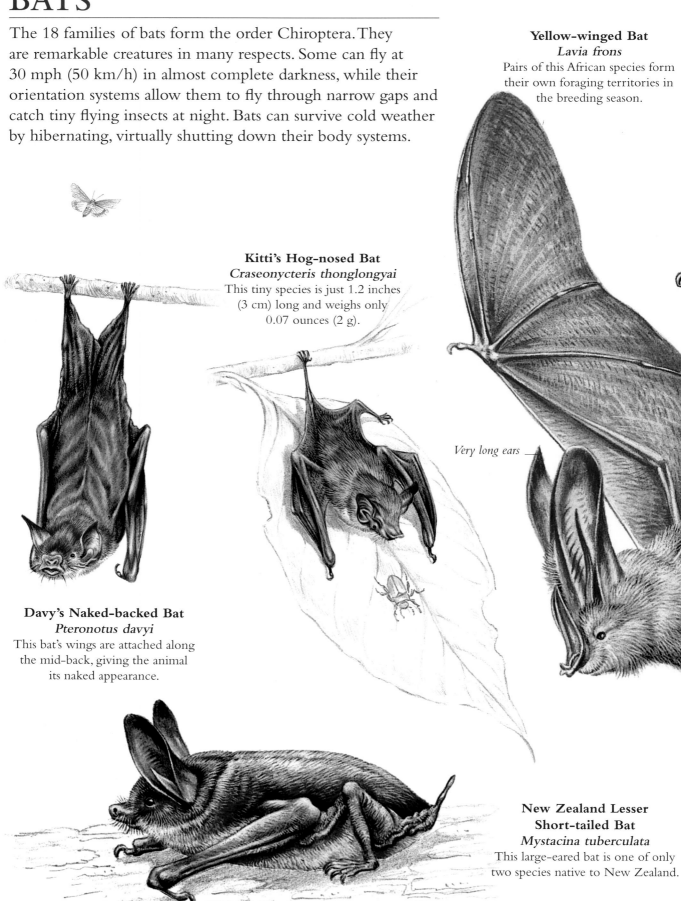

Yellow-winged Bat
Lavia frons
Pairs of this African species form their own foraging territories in the breeding season.

Kitti's Hog-nosed Bat
Craseonycteris thonglongyai
This tiny species is just 1.2 inches (3 cm) long and weighs only 0.07 ounces (2 g).

Very long ears

Davy's Naked-backed Bat
Pteronotus davyi
This bat's wings are attached along the mid-back, giving the animal its naked appearance.

New Zealand Lesser Short-tailed Bat
Mystacina tuberculata
This large-eared bat is one of only two species native to New Zealand.

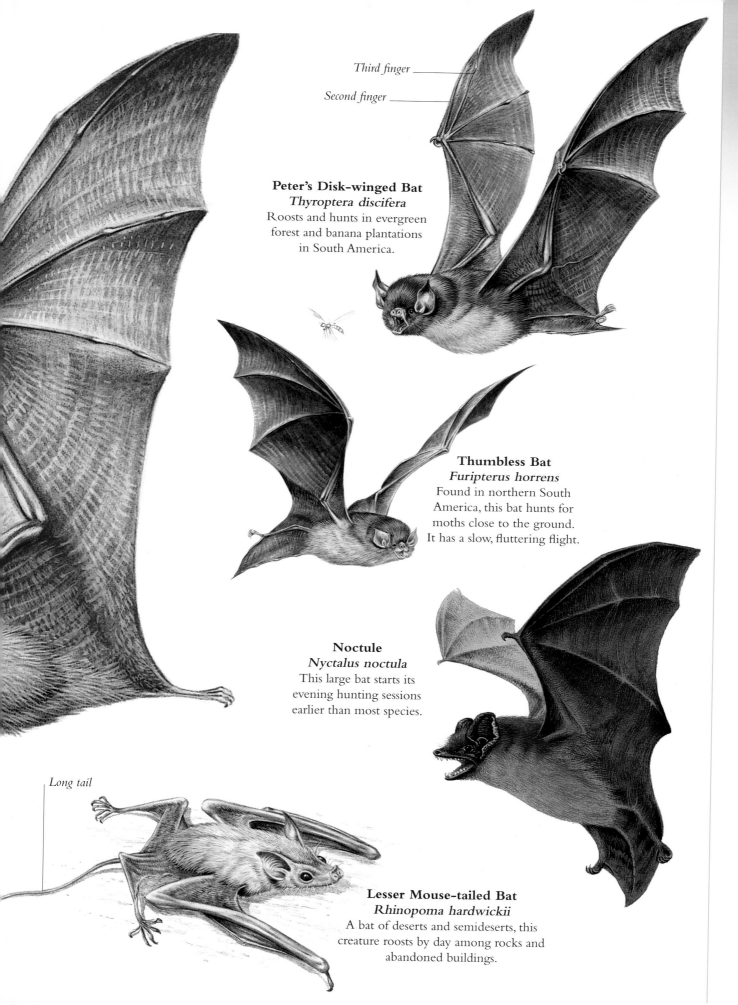

Third finger

Second finger

Peter's Disk-winged Bat
Thyroptera discifera
Roosts and hunts in evergreen
forest and banana plantations
in South America.

Thumbless Bat
Furipterus horrens
Found in northern South
America, this bat hunts for
moths close to the ground.
It has a slow, fluttering flight.

Noctule
Nyctalus noctula
This large bat starts its
evening hunting sessions
earlier than most species.

Long tail

Lesser Mouse-tailed Bat
Rhinopoma hardwickii
A bat of deserts and semideserts, this
creature roosts by day among rocks and
abandoned buildings.

BATS

Bats live in most terrestrial habitats apart from Antarctica, the most northerly latitudes, and the highest mountains. Most use sophisticated echolocation techniques to navigate and hunt for insects. However, the flying foxes (family Pteropodidae) feed mainly on fruit and nectar; they have well-developed vision and make little use of echolocation.

Gray Bat
Myotis grisescens
This North American species hibernates in winter.

Big Brown Bat
Eptesicus fuscus
Roosting by day in hollow trees, this echolocator hunts insects at night.

Spectral Bat
Vampyrum spectrum
A formidable predator, this "false vampire" predates small mammals, reptiles, and large insects in northern South America.

Long ears for echolocation

Mexican Long-nosed Bat
Leptonycteris nivalis
A migrant species, it moves between central and northern Mexico in spring and fall.

Parnell's Mustached Bat
Pteronotus parnellii
Roosts in caves and tunnels, primarily in moist areas.

Fringe-lipped Bat
Trachops cirrhosus
This bat picks insects, frogs, and lizards from vegetation.

Ryukyu Flying Fox
Pteropus dasymallus
Uses its good eyesight
to find fruits and flowers
on which to feed.

Large eye

Greater Bulldog Bat
Noctilio leporinus
Using echolocation to detect
ripples on the surface of
lakes and rivers, this bat
swoops down to grab fish
swimming near the surface.

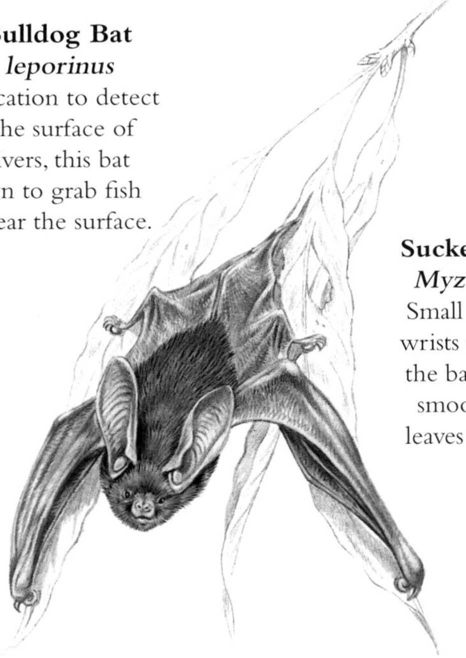

Sucker-footed Bat
Myzopoda aurita
Small suckers on the
wrists and ankles help
the bat adhere to the
smooth surfaces of
leaves in Madagascar.

Fish plucked from water

WEASELS, OTTERS, AND ALLIES

The family Mustelidae comprises weasels, polecats, and otters, as well as martens, badgers, and wolverines. All mustelids are fiercely carnivorous and very strong. For example, a weasel is capable of running at speed while carrying prey more than half its own weight. A Lion could never achieve this feat. In the wild, mustelids live on all continents apart from Australasia.

American Mink
Neovison vison
Occurring naturally in North America, this fierce predator has become naturalized across much of Europe and Central and East Asia.

Black-footed Ferret
Mustela nigripes
The animal shown is about to enter the burrow of a prairie dog, a favored food item.

Clasping a shell

Indian Smooth-coated Otter
Lutrogale perspicillata
This species has heavily webbed but highly dextrous forepaws, ideal for swimming and grabbing prey.

Patagonian Weasel
Lyncodon patagonicus
An inhabitant of pampas grasslands in Argentina and Chile, this weasel has been kept by farmers as a working pet to control rats.

African Striped Weasel
Poecilogale albinucha
This nocturnal hunter lives in forests, wetlands, and grasslands in sub-Saharan Africa. It grows to 16 inches (40 cm), half this length being its cream and brown tail.

Marbled Polecat
Vormela peregusna
Relatively large ears, short limbs and long, strong claws are characteristic of this species of Central Asia and southeast Europe. Active mostly during the early morning and evening, the polecat relies mostly on its sensitive sense of smell to seek out prey.

Lesser Grison
Galictis cuja
This species has webbed feet with five toes ending in sharp, curved claws.

Striped Polecat (above)
Ictonyx striatus
Also known as the Zorilla, its defence mechanism includes spraying aggressors with noxious fluids from anal stink glands.

Sea Otter (left)
Enhydra lutris
Characteristically, this individual is floating on its back and crushing a bivalve shell with a stone.

EARED SEALS AND WALRUS

Sea lions and fur seals (part of the family Otariidae) are distinguished from true seals by their use of the foreflippers as the principal means of propulsion through the water. Most sea lions are larger than most fur seals and have blunter snouts. Sea lions' flippers are usually shorter than those of fur seals. The Walrus (Odobenidae) is very large and has prominent tusks.

South American Fur Seal
Arctocephalus australis
Female fur seals give birth to a single pup between mid-October and December and often mate again a week after the birth.

Two male Walruses having a stabbing duel with their tusks

Walrus
Odobenus rosmarus
Heavily mustached above gleaming tusks, and capable of a wide range of roars and grunts, Walruses make a dramatic first impression.

California Sea Lion (left)
Zalophus californianus
An adult male is dark chestnut
brown and weighs around
660 pounds (300 kg).

Steller Sea Lion (above)
Eumetopias jubatus
This sea lion lives in the northern
Pacific. Both males and females are
light brown to reddish brown.

**South American
Sea Lion**
Otaria flavescens
Dives of 574 feet (175 m)
and more than 7 minutes
have been recorded for
this species.

**New Zealand
Sea Lion**
Phocarctos hookeri
Full-grown males are
blackish brown and
weigh up to 990
pounds (450 kg).

Northern Fur Seal
Callorhinus ursinus
The short muzzle of this
cold-water seal gives it a
distinctive profile.

TRUE SEALS

There are 19 species of true seals (family Phocidae). Most inhabit oceanic waters at high latitudes in both hemispheres, although the monk seals of Mediterranean and Hawaiian regions live in warmer waters. True seals can dive to great depths in search of prey, which includes fish, shellfish, and cephalopods such as squid.

Dark silvery gray coat, darker above, and mottled with black, gray, and whitish blotches

1.

3.

Pale bands around the neck, flippers, and hips

2.

Antarctic seals
Ross Seal, *Ommatophoca rossii* (above left), is a thick-necked, short-muzzled species. The canines and two large protruding incisor teeth of **Weddell Seals, *Leptonychotes weddellii*** (above right), are often worn from sawing at ice holes.

Northern Elephant Seal
Mirounga angustirostrus
The size difference between males and females is enormous: a full-grown male can weigh up to 5,950 pounds (2.7 tonnes) but a female will grow to no more than about 1,980 pounds (0.9 tonnes).

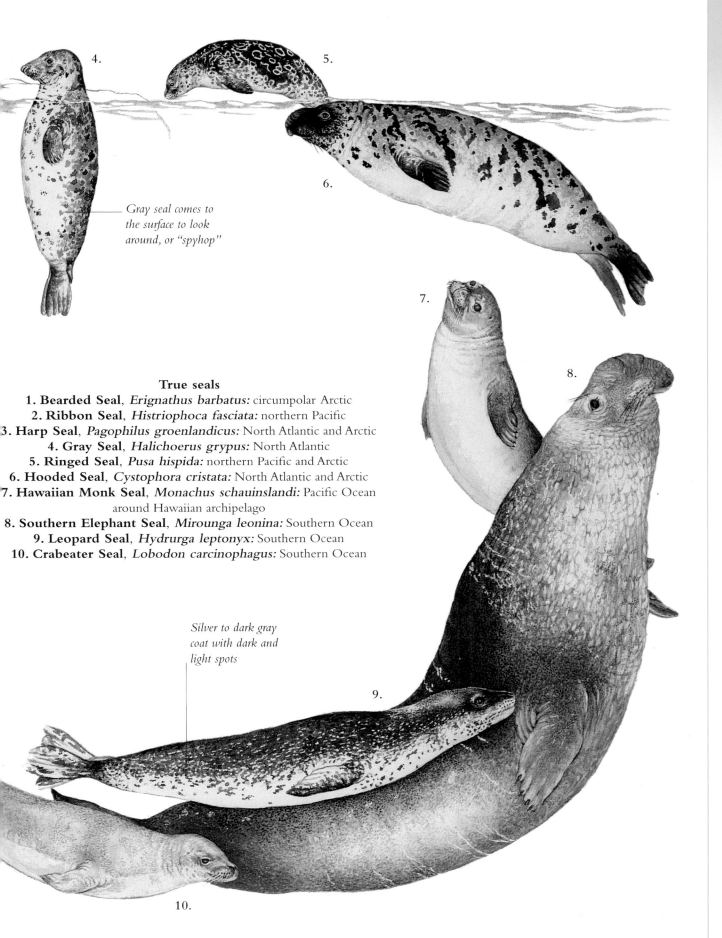

4.

5.

6.

7.

8.

9.

10.

Gray seal comes to the surface to look around, or "spyhop"

True seals
1. **Bearded Seal**, *Erignathus barbatus:* circumpolar Arctic
2. **Ribbon Seal**, *Histriophoca fasciata:* northern Pacific
3. **Harp Seal**, *Pagophilus groenlandicus:* North Atlantic and Arctic
4. **Gray Seal**, *Halichoerus grypus:* North Atlantic
5. **Ringed Seal**, *Pusa hispida:* northern Pacific and Arctic
6. **Hooded Seal**, *Cystophora cristata:* North Atlantic and Arctic
7. **Hawaiian Monk Seal**, *Monachus schauinslandi:* Pacific Ocean
around Hawaiian archipelago
8. **Southern Elephant Seal**, *Mirounga leonina:* Southern Ocean
9. **Leopard Seal**, *Hydrurga leptonyx:* Southern Ocean
10. **Crabeater Seal**, *Lobodon carcinophagus:* Southern Ocean

Silver to dark gray coat with dark and light spots

BEARS

The bear family (Ursidae) contains the world's largest terrestrial carnivores, Brown Bears and Polar Bears, but the latter is the only bear species to consume an all-meat diet. Bears rely more on strength than speed when feeding. Most climb trees to forage or sleep, the exceptions being Polar Bears and most North American Brown Bears.

Brown Bear
Ursus arctos
Pacific Salmon, swimming upstream to their spawning grounds, form an important element of the diet of Brown (Grizzly) Bears on the western coast of North America.

White "V" on chest

Asian Black Bear
Ursus thibetanus
Although mostly herbivorous, this species may—as here—eat carrion.

Andean Bear
Tremarctos ornatus
South America's only bear often climbs trees in search of fruit.

Layer of fat and thick coat protect against the bitter Arctic winter

Shaggy coat

Polar Bear
Ursus maritimus
This is the world's largest bear, weighing up to 1,323 pounds (600 kg) and with a head-body length of up to 9 feet (2.5 m).

Sloth Bear
Melursus ursinus
This South Asian species uses its long, curved claws and flexible snout to forage for insects.

Sun Bear
Helarctos malayanus
The smallest of the world's bears is here shown licking termites from a mound it has just broken open.

Giant Panda
Ailuropoda melanoleuca
Cool, damp bamboo forests in China, between 4,920–11,150 feet (1,500–3,400 m), are the habitat of this iconic, rare, bamboo-eater.

DOGS

The dog family (Canidae) comprises wolves, coyotes, jackals, foxes, and wild dogs. This successful group of animals has representatives on every continent. Dogs evolved for the fast pursuit of prey in open grasslands, though some species now inhabit forest habitats. Most have long, bushy tails and long legs. They range in size from the tiny Fennec Fox to the pack-hunting Gray Wolf.

Arctic Fox
Vulpes lagopus
This individual is in its gray-brown and silver summer pelt; in winter it will be all-white.

Golden Jackal (left)
Canis aureus

Side-striped Jackal
Canis adustus
This is a species of grassland habitats in Central Africa.

Black-backed Jackals
Canis mesomelas
In most dog species, social interactions are important. Here, two young jackals are playing a tail-pulling game.

Red Foxes
Vulpes vulpes
1. Red form, typical of high latitudes
2. "Silver fox," the widespread but relatively rare melanistic form
3. "Cross fox," the partly melanistic form is more common than the silver morph

Small-eared Dog
Atelocynus microtis
This dog is adapted for life in
undisturbed lowland rain forest
in South America.

Culpeo
*Pseudalopex
culpaeus*
A species that lives
high in the Andes
Mountains.

Crab-eating Fox
Cerdocyon thous
This South American
fox eats a broad range
of food, including crabs
during the wet season.

Chilla
Pseudalopex griseus
An inhabitant of
grasslands and scrub
in the foothills of the
Andes Mountains.

Pampas Fox
Pseudalopex gymnocercus
This is a species that lives on
South American grasslands.

European Gray Wolf
Canis lupus lupus
Wolves howl to
advertise their presence
to other members of
the species.

Tibetan Gray Wolf
Canis lupus chanco
Thought by some to be the
ancestor of the domestic dog,
this form has been seen at
altitudes up to 10,000 feet
(3,048 m) in the Himalayas.

Wolfdog
Canis lupus
As its name suggests, this dog
is a cross between a Gray
Wolf and a Siberian Husky
domesticated dog.

CATS AND HYENAS

The cats (family Felidae) are the most carnivorous of the mammals, sitting at the summit of many food pyramids. Built to hunt, they have blunt, flattened faces, large eyes and ears, and claws that can be unsheathed. There are just four species of hyenas (family Hyaenidae), tropical hunters with complex social systems. Hyenas have extraordinarily strong teeth and jaws, allowing them to crush bones to extract the nutritious marrow.

Leopard
Panthera pardus
To keep their prey from scavengers, Leopards often store their kills in trees.

Small North American cats
Lynx, *Lynx lynx* (above right), has a plainer coat than the closely related **Bobcat,** *Lynx rufus,* a species of more open environments.

Jaguar
Panthera onca
Jaguars often bury their prey in leaf litter on the forest floor.

Lion
Panthera leo
Adult males (above right) dominate once a prey item has been downed, although lionesses are responsible for the majority of kills, sometimes hunting cooperatively.

Cheetah
Acinonyx jubatus
This is the fastest
animal on land.

Ocelot
Leopardus pardalis
This nocturnal New World
species fights fiercely—
sometimes to the death—in
territorial disputes.

Tiger
Panthera tigris
The most formidable big cat
of all roars to warn other
Tigers of its presence.

Brown Hyena
Hyaena brunnea
A shaggy species with
characteristic horizontal
lines on its legs.

Bobcat
Lynx rufus
Bobcats eat prey ranging in size
from insects to deer, though rabbits
and hares are preferred.

Spotted Hyena
Crocuta crocuta
Typical for the species, a
pack of hyenas hunts
down a zebra on the
African savanna.

MONGOOSES AND CIVETS

Distributed throughout much of sub-Saharan Africa and southern Asia, mongooses (family Herpestidae) are slender carnivores, whose diet ranges from insects to crabs, and reptiles to birds' eggs. The civets (family Viverridae) are nocturnal foragers and ambush predators in Africa and South and Southeast Asia.

White-tailed Mongoose
Ichneumia albicauda
A resident of sub-Saharan Africa, this is the largest mongoose of all.

Bushy-tailed Mongoose
Bdeogale crassicauda
This individual, in "high-sit" position, is sniffing the air for the scent of other animals.

Ring-tailed Mongoose
Galidia elegans
This individual is in fast-trotting mode.

Common Dwarf Mongoose
Helogale parvula
An adult feeds a beetle to a juvenile.

Selous' Mongoose
Paracynictis selousi
A solitary species from southern Africa (right).

Egyptian Mongoose
Herpestes ichneumon
Eggs are an important part of the diet of this native of Africa.

Marsh Mongoose
Atilax paludinosus
This animal is scent-marking a rock to advertise its presence to other mongooses.

African Linsang
Poiana richardsonii
This is one of just two species of
linsangs, whose diet includes nestlings.

Banded Palm Civet
Hemigalus derbyanus
A distinctively marked nocturnal
species of Southeast Asia.

Oriental Civet
Viverra tangalunga
This individual's
dorsal crest is erect.

Asian Palm Civet
*Paradoxurus
hermaphroditus*

Binturong
Arctictis binturong
The animal grasps a branch with its
prehensile tail while foraging for fruit.

ZEBRAS, HORSES, AND TAPIRS

Zebras and horses (family Equidae) are grazers of grasses and other ground vegetation. Their long legs allow them to run fast. There are just four species of tapirs (family Tapiridae), which have a versatile prehensile trunk and acute senses of hearing and smell—though their sight is not good. Tapirs live in South America and Southeast Asia.

Zebra body language
1. Mountain Zebra, *Equus zebra*
A young male presents a submissive face to an adult male.
2. Plains Zebra, *Equus burchellii*
A male displays a "low-head" posture to drive mares forward.
3. Grevy's Zebra, *Equus grevyi*
A female in heat in a receptive position with her hindlegs slightly splayed.

Przewalski's Horse
Equus przewalski
This is considered to be the
true wild horse and the
ancestor of all domestic horses.

*Disruptive coloration
for disguise in the forest*

Malayan Tapir
Tapirus indicus
Destruction of dense primary rain
forest in Southeast Asia threatens
this species' survival.

African Ass
Equus asinus
This ass is performing
an aggressive kick
threat with its ears
held back.

Prehensile trunk

Mountain Tapir
Tapirus pinchaque
This animal's prime habitat is cloud
forest and paramo grassland in the
Andes Mountains.

Ears held back

Baird's Tapir
Tapirus bairdii
The juvenile (left) of this endangered
species is distinctively marked with white
spots and stripes.

Brazilian Tapir
Tapirus terrestris
This tapir lives in lowland rain forests
and lower montane forests in the
Amazon and Orinoco basins.

DEER

More than 40 species of deer (family Cervidae) live in forest and grassland habitats in North and South America and Eurasia. The antlers of male deer distinguish the animals from other ruminants. Antlers are shed and regrown every year. All four species of musk deer (Moschidae) live in East Asia. Musk deer do not have antlers but males have long, protruding canine teeth.

Elk, or Moose
Alces alces
This, the largest deer, weighs up to 1,763 pounds (800 kg). The male's antlers are large, branched, and palmate.

Reeve's Muntjac
Muntiacus reevesi
Native to China and Taiwan, this species has been introduced to England, where it thrives.

Roe Deer
Capreolus capreolus
In summer, the Roe Deer's plain grayish-fawn winter coat is replaced by brighter fox-red fur.

Chital
Axis axis
A South Asian woodland and forest-edge species with lyre-shaped antlers.

Himalayan Musk Deer
Moschus chrysogaster
This is an endangered species native to China.

Chinese Water Deer
Hydropotes inermis
Lives in swamps, reedbeds, and damp grasslands in China and Korea.

Sika Deer
Cervus nippon
Naturally an East Asian species, the
Sika has been introduced and now
thrives in other parts of the world.

**Red Brocket (left)
and White-tailed Deer**
Mazama americana
and *Odocoileus virginianus*

*Males' branched
antlers larger than
females' and shed from
November to April*

Marsh Deer
Blastocerus dichotomus
The reddish summer coat is
shown; in winter it is
duller brown.

Caribou
Rangifer tarandus
This high latitude species lives in
woodland, forest edge, and—in
summer—tundra. Both sexes have
antlers, the males' being larger.

Southern Pudu
Pudu pudu
This is the smallest deer—just 14 inches (35 cm)
tall at the shoulder and weighing 18 pounds (8 kg).

Pampas Deer
Ozotoceros bezoarticus
Pampas Deer live on open, grassy
plains in southern South America.

WILD CATTLE

Wild cattle, spiral-horned antelopes, and four-horned antelopes (family Bovidae) are three tribes that look different, though scientific analyses have shown that there are many structural similarities between them. Wild cattle have a diet of grasses, and spiral-horned antelopes eat leaves, bud, fruits, bark, and roots. Present-day cattle are descended from the now-extinct Auroch.

Auroch
Bos primigenius
Domesticated cattle are descended from Aurochs, the last of which died out in the 17th century.

Nilgai
Boselaphus tragocamelus
This Indian species is a member of the tribe Boselaphini (four-horned antelopes), which is closely related to the Bovini (wild cattle).

Kouprey
Bos sauveli
First described by zoologists in 1937 and last seen in Cambodia, Vietnam, and Laos, this species may now be extinct.

Saola, or Vu Quang Ox
Pseudoryx nghetinhensis
This small bovid was first seen
by scientists in dense forest
in Vietnam in 1993. Its
population is believed to
be no more than
a few hundred.

Spiral horn

Common Eland
Taurotragus oryx
This nomadic spiral-horned
antelope of the African savannas is
now only found in game reserves.

Wild Water Buffalo
Bubalus arnee
Flexible fetlock joints make the
Water Buffalo nimble in soft mud.

American Bison
Bison bison
Virtually wiped out by
hunting in the 19th century,
small numbers survive in
North American refuges.

GRAZING ANTELOPES

More than 20 species of grazing antelopes (family Bovidae) grace the great savannas of Africa, ranging across wet and dry grasslands and forest edge, up to an altitude of 16,400 feet (5,000 m). In the wettest areas it is only the intense grazing and browsing pressure of herbivores such as antelopes—along with frequent burning—that keeps the grasslands from becoming forest.

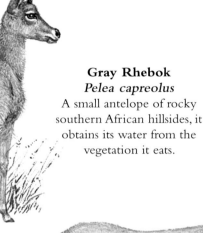

Gray Rhebok
Pelea capreolus
A small antelope of rocky southern African hillsides, it obtains its water from the vegetation it eats.

Uganda Kob
Kobus kob thomasi
A male holds its head high as it approaches a female during the breeding season.

Coke's Hartebeest
Alcelaphus busephalus cokii
One of a dozen subspecies of hartebeest, Coke's is an animal of coarse grassland and open woodland in East Africa.

Head bowed in submissive posture

Impala
Aepyceros melampus
The Impala is the quintessential antelope, light-limbed and graceful. This is a territorial male.

Bontebok
Damaliscus pygargus
This individual is initiating a butting contest with another male by dropping to its knees.

Sable Antelope
Hippotragus niger
The male is black with a
white belly and has two long
scythelike horns.

Roan Antelope
Hippotragus equinus
The ears of this
forest-edge antelope
are long with a tuft of
hair at the tip.

Addax
Addax nasomaculatus
Critically endangered
and facing extinction, the
North African Addax lives
in some of the most
arid places on Earth.

Gemsbok
Oryx gazella
During courtship the
male gives a ritual
kick with its foreleg.

*Black on
forehead*

Topi
Damaliscus lunatus
The coat of this elegant antelope
is mahogany red, with bold
patches of black.

Blue Wildebeest
Connochaetes taurinus
The horns curve downward laterally
and then point upward and inward.

GAZELLES AND GOATS

Gazelles (family Bovidae) comprise some of the most abundant, rare, and least-known of all hooved animals. They occupy habitats from dense forest to desert. The goat antelopes (also bovids) are usually stocky and gregarious animals. Some have small horns but others, such as Musk Oxen, are long and curved. Males are larger and have longer horns.

White patch on neck

Dama Gazelle
Gazella dama
A rare species with unusually long legs and neck for a gazelle.

**Beira (foreground)
and Klipspringer**
Dorcatragus megalotis
and *Oreotragus oreotragus*
The Beira's rubbery hooves are adapted for life in rocky deserts in Ethiopia and Somalia. The Klipspringer's thick fur gives it a stocky appearance.

Steenbok
Raphicerus campestris
This individual is scent-marking with its preorbital gland.

Twisted horn

Blackbuck
Antilope cervicapra
Only the male Blackbuck has these beautifully twisted horns.

Distinctive black flank stripe

Thomson's Gazelle (left)
Eudorcas thomsonii
This gazelle of the grassy plains of East Africa migrates in large numbers in search of better grazing.

Argalis
Ovis ammon
A goat antelope of the
bleak Tibetan plateau and
Outer Mongolia.

*Each horn grows up to
3 feet (91 cm) long*

Takin
Budorcas taxicolor
Lives in montane meadows and
bamboo forests on steep terrain in
southwest China and Burma.

Musk Ox
Ovibos moschatus
This shaggy animal has dense,
long fur, with some hair strands
being up to 2 feet (62 cm) long.

Goat antelopes
1. Mountain Goat
Oreamnos americanus
mountains, North America.
2. Chamois
Rupicapra rupicapra
alpine forests and meadows,
southern Europe and Turkey.
3. Alpine Ibex
Capra ibex
mountains and deserts,
Central Europe, Middle East,
and northeast Africa.
4. Japanese Serow
Capricornis crispus
varied habitats, Japan and Taiwan.
5. Wild Goat
Capra aegagrus
varied habitats, southeast Europe,
Middle East, and South Asia.
6. Urial
Ovis orientalis vignei:
hills and deserts, South Asia.
7. Barbary Sheep
Ammotragus lervia
mountains and high deserts,
North Africa.

DOLPHINS

Dolphins (family Delphinidae) are generally small to medium-sized mammals with well-developed beaks and a central, sickle-shaped dorsal fin. They have a single blowhole on top of the head, and teeth in both jaws. In fact, dolphins and river dolphins are toothed whales. Each of the four river dolphins has its own family (Platanistidae, Lipotidae, Iniidae, and Pontoporiidae); one species is probably now extinct.

1.

Longest beak, relative to body length, of any cetacean

Franciscana
Pontoporia blainvillei
Lives close to the coast of eastern South America, from central Brazil to northern Argentina.

Very shallow dorsal fin

Amazon Dolphin
Inia geoffrensis
A native of the Amazon and Orinoco river basins, males of this species carry clumps of twigs in mating displays.

Striking black and white patterning

Risso's Dolphin
Grampus griseus
This small, beakless dolphin is found in all the world's major oceans.

A selection of dolphins
1. **Atlantic White-sided Dolphin**, *Lagenorhynchus acutus*
2. **Atlantic Spotted Dolphin**, *Stenella frontalis*
3. **Short-beaked Common Dolphin**, *Delphinus delphis*
4. **Northern Right Whale Dolphin**, *Lissodelphis borealis*
5. **Dusky Dolphin**, *Lagenorhynchus obscurus*
6. **Atlantic Hump-backed Dolphin**, *Sousa teuszii*
7. **Melon-headed Whale**, *Peponocephala electra*
8. **Commerson's Dolphin**, *Cephalorhynchus commersonii*

Ganges Dolphin
Platanista gangetica
A native of the Ganges and
Indus river systems, this species
is declining in numbers.

Yangtze River Dolphin
Lipotes vexillifer
It is likely that this Chinese
species is now extinct.

Killer Whale, or Orca
Orcinus orca
An apex predator that hunts prey as
large as adult seals, the Killer Whale
often hunts cooperatively.

False Killer Whale
Pseudorca crassidens
This species lives in tropical and
warm temperate regions of the
Indian, Pacific, and Atlantic oceans.

PORPOISES AND BELUGA

The six porpoises (family Phocoenidae) are closely related to true dolphins but have a shorter beak. Porpoises are small, with no member of the family being more than 8 feet (2.5 m) long. The Beluga is one of the two "white whales" (family Monodontidae). Belugas inhabit the cold waters of the Arctic Ocean and are among the most social of the cetaceans.

Rounded head shape typical of all porpoises

Vaquita
Phocoena sinus
This critically endangered species is the smallest of the porpoises and is found only in the Upper Gulf of California.

Finless Porpoise
Neophocaena phocaenoides
This pale gray species lives in Indo-Pacific waters from the Persian Gulf to Indonesia, and north to Japan.

Burmeister's Porpoise
Phocoena spinipinnis
This porpoise hardly disturbs the water when it comes up to breath, so it is very hard to catch sight of one.

Calf

Beluga
Delphinapterus leucas
From June to September, Belugas gather in hundreds and thousands to give birth to their calves in wide river estuaries around the Arctic Ocean.

Dall's Porpoise
Phocoenoides dalli
A species of the northern Pacific Ocean, its patterning is reminiscent of a very small Killer Whale.

Spectacled Porpoise
Phocoena dioptrica
Males of this Southern Ocean porpoise have a larger dorsal fin than the females.

Harbor Porpoise
Phocoena phocoena
These porpoises feed on fish and squid in the water column and on the sea floor.

BEAKED WHALES, SPERM WHALE, AND NARWHAL

The beaked whales (family Ziphiidae) probably forage at or close to the sea bed in water depths of 3,300 feet (1,005 m) or more. Dives of up to 30 minutes' duration are commonplace. The Narwhal (family Monodontidae) is a cold-water species of the Arctic Ocean, where it hunts flatfish, codfish, shrimp, and squid.

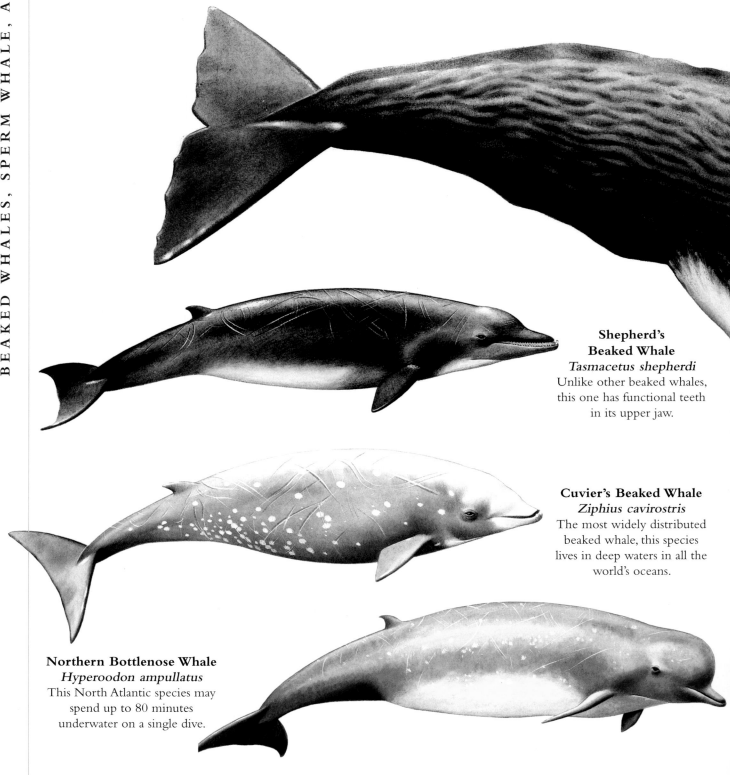

Shepherd's Beaked Whale
Tasmacetus shepherdi
Unlike other beaked whales, this one has functional teeth in its upper jaw.

Cuvier's Beaked Whale
Ziphius cavirostris
The most widely distributed beaked whale, this species lives in deep waters in all the world's oceans.

Northern Bottlenose Whale
Hyperoodon ampullatus
This North Atlantic species may spend up to 80 minutes underwater on a single dive.

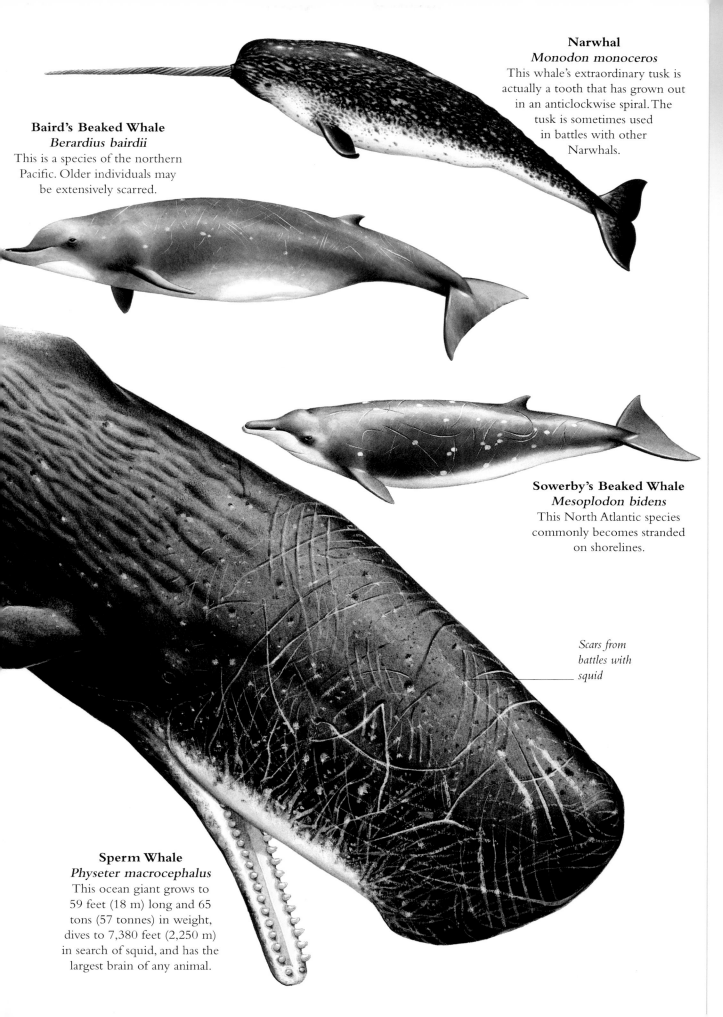

Narwhal
Monodon monoceros
This whale's extraordinary tusk is actually a tooth that has grown out in an anticlockwise spiral. The tusk is sometimes used in battles with other Narwhals.

Baird's Beaked Whale
Berardius bairdii
This is a species of the northern Pacific. Older individuals may be extensively scarred.

Sowerby's Beaked Whale
Mesoplodon bidens
This North Atlantic species commonly becomes stranded on shorelines.

Scars from battles with squid

Sperm Whale
Physeter macrocephalus
This ocean giant grows to 59 feet (18 m) long and 65 tons (57 tonnes) in weight, dives to 7,380 feet (2,250 m) in search of squid, and has the largest brain of any animal.

BALEEN WHALES

There are 14 species of baleen whales in four families. The baleen plates (flexible strips of protein hanging from the jaws) filter planktonic organisms, larger invertebrates, and small fish from sea water as it enters the whale's mouth. Baleen whales inhabit all the world's oceans and include the largest creature on the planet—the Blue Whale.

Northern Right Whale
Eubalaena glacialis
This species often has patches of rough, thickened skin, which are heavily infested with crustacean parasites called cyamids.

Bryde's Whale
Balaenoptera edeni
One of the smaller baleens, Bryde's is still very large, growing to 36 feet (11 m) and 22 tons (20 tonnes).

Single calf born in alternative years after 13-month gestation

Gray Whale
Eschrichtius robustus
Unusually for the baleen whales, this species lives mostly in coastal waters that are relatively shallow (less than 330 feet, 100 m).

Fin Whale
Balaenoptera physalus
This large whale grows up to 80 feet (24 m) in length and 88 tons (80 tonnes) in weight. It has 260–470 baleen plates.

Pale skin on belly contrasts with gray above

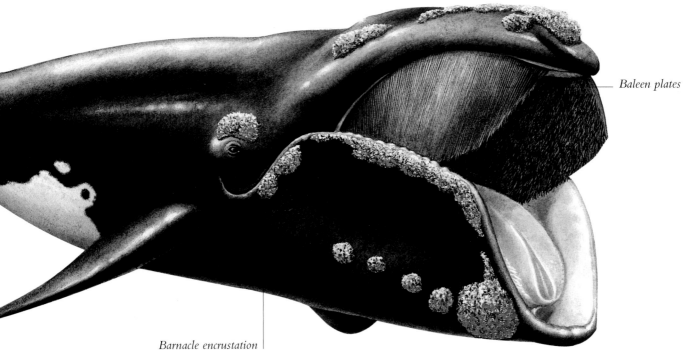

Baleen plates

Barnacle encrustation

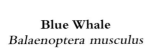

Blue Whale
Balaenoptera musculus
The biggest whale of all can grow to 90 feet (27 m) in length and 165 tons (150 tonnes) in weight. The world population is 10,000–25,000.

Northern Minke Whale
Balaenoptera acutorostrata
This species has 230–350 baleen plates and 50–70 throat grooves.

Blue whales have 270–395 blue-black baleen plates

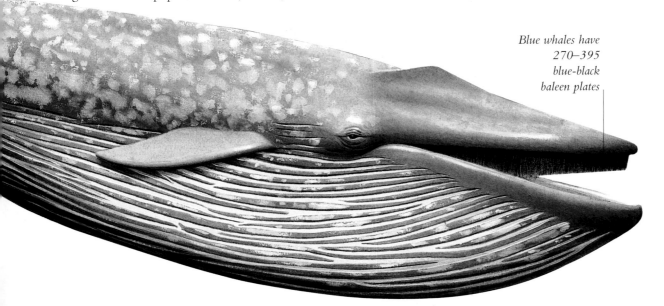

WHAT IS A BIRD?

Birds (class Aves) are warm-blooded, feathered, reproduce sexually, and lay eggs. Their forelimbs have evolved into wings, which provide most species with their primary means of movement. The 10,000 or so species show a wide variety of anatomy and color, but the range of forms is less varied than that of mammals. This is thought to be because of the constraints imposed by the requirements of flight.

▶ BODY PLAN

Many aspects of a bird's form, structure, and organic functions are remarkable, having evolved to enable flight. For example, birds' hollow bones are lighter by far than those of mammals. And, in respiration, a bird replaces almost all the air in its lungs with each breath.

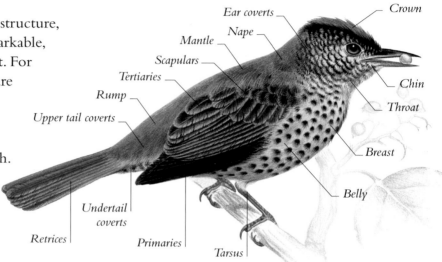

Ear coverts
Crown
Nape
Mantle
Scapulars
Tertiaries
Rump
Upper tail coverts
Chin
Throat
Breast
Belly
Undertail coverts
Retrices
Primaries
Tarsus

▼ DIGESTIVE SYSTEM

After being ingested, food passes into the crop. Exclusive to birds, this organ stores food, either passing it to the stomach or retaining it for regurgitation later. In the stomach, food is processed in the proventriculus and then in the gizzard.

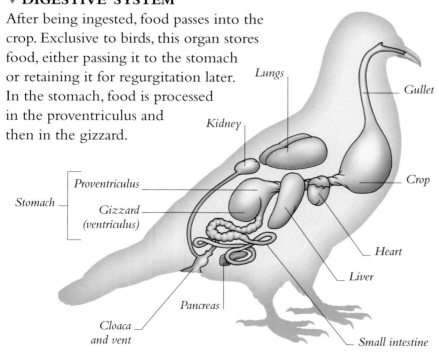

Lungs
Gullet
Kidney
Proventriculus
Stomach
Gizzard
(ventriculus)
Crop
Heart
Liver
Pancreas
Cloaca
and vent
Small intestine

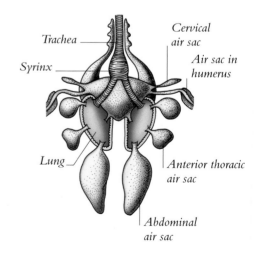

Trachea
Cervical air sac
Syrinx
Air sac in humerus
Lung
Anterior thoracic air sac
Abdominal air sac

▲ RESPIRATORY SYSTEM

Birds' relatively small lungs are supplemented by multiple air sacs, which maximize the diffusion of oxygen into the bloodstream.

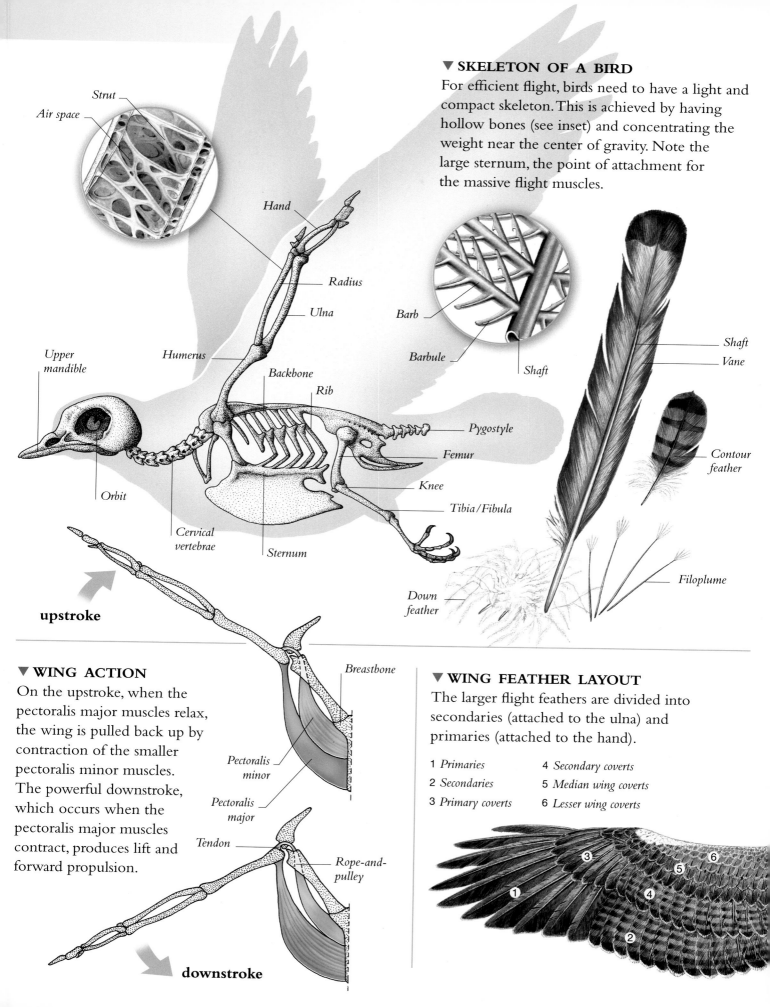

Strut

Air space

▼ SKELETON OF A BIRD

For efficient flight, birds need to have a light and compact skeleton. This is achieved by having hollow bones (see inset) and concentrating the weight near the center of gravity. Note the large sternum, the point of attachment for the massive flight muscles.

Hand

Radius

Ulna

Humerus

Backbone

Rib

Barb

Barbule

Shaft

Shaft

Vane

Upper mandible

Pygostyle

Femur

Knee

Contour feather

Orbit

Tibia / Fibula

Cervical vertebrae

Sternum

Filoplume

Down feather

upstroke

▼ WING ACTION

On the upstroke, when the pectoralis major muscles relax, the wing is pulled back up by contraction of the smaller pectoralis minor muscles. The powerful downstroke, which occurs when the pectoralis major muscles contract, produces lift and forward propulsion.

Breastbone

Pectoralis minor

Pectoralis major

Tendon

Rope-and-pulley

downstroke

▼ WING FEATHER LAYOUT

The larger flight feathers are divided into secondaries (attached to the ulna) and primaries (attached to the hand).

1 *Primaries*
2 *Secondaries*
3 *Primary coverts*
4 *Secondary coverts*
5 *Median wing coverts*
6 *Lesser wing coverts*

RATITES AND TINAMOUS

The ratities are a mixed bunch of flightless birds—ranging in size from the huge Ostrich of African savannas to New Zealand's diminutive kiwis. Emus and cassowaries also live in Australasia and rheas in South America. Tinamous (family Tinamidae) can fly, but not very well. These South American ground-dwellers rely on camouflage plumage to avoid detection by predators on the forest floor.

Little Tinamou
Crypturellus soui
Lives in forests in a vast area of Central and northern South America. Its young are precocial, running almost as soon as they have hatched.

Small-billed Tinamou
Crypturellus parvirostris
This is a bird of savanna habitats and even cultivated fields in Brazil.

Great Tinamou
Tinamus major
Parental care is provided by the male alone, incubating the eggs and looking after the chicks until they are three weeks old.

Ostrich
Struthio camelus
The world's largest bird grows to 8 feet (2.5 m) tall and 254 pounds (115 kg) in weight. It can run at 30 mph (50 km/h).

Red-winged Tinamou
Rhyncotus rufescens
The bright rufous primary feathers on this bird are only visible when it flies.

Lesser Rhea
Pterocnemia pennata
The two species of rheas (this and
the Greater Rhea), both native to
South America, are the most
Ostrich-like of the ratites.

Emu
Dromaius novaehollandiae
Feeds on seeds, fruits, flowers, roots,
and large insects by day in open forest
and semi-arid plains in Australia.

Recently fledged chick

Wattle

Northern Cassowary
Casuarius unappendiculatus
Cassowaries play a vital role in the ecology of
their native New Guinea, dispersing the seeds of
many trees. They are large, flightless, forest birds.
Head and wattle color varies between individuals.

PENGUINS

The 17 species of penguins (family Spheniscidae) are flightless but superbly adapted for life at sea. They are streamlined and their wings are used as strong flippers to propel them at speed through the water. Penguins are well insulated against the cold and are capable of deep dives. Many are colonial nesters in Antarctica, though Galápagos Penguins live close to the equator in the Pacific Ocean.

Chinstrap Penguin
Pygoscelis antarctica
Chinstrap Penguins nest in colonies in Antarctica and on islands in the Southern Ocean. Here, an adult is being harassed by two Snowy Sheathbills *(Chionis alba)*.

Jackass Penguin
Spheniscus demersus
Confined to southern African waters, this penguin gets its name for its donkey-like braying calls.

Adélie Penguin
Pygoscelis adeliae
During the October–January breeding season these penguins gather in huge colonies around Antarctic coasts.

Rockhopper Penguin
Eudyptes chrysocome
The parents divide egg-incubation duties, then the male broods the two chicks for up to 25 days while the female hunts for food.

Chicks fledge at around 10 weeks of age

Yellow-eyed Penguin
Megadyptes antipodes
The least social penguin, and one of
the rarest, this species breeds in forest
and scrub on New Zealand's South
Island and on small offshore islands.

*Penguin chicks retain
their brown, downy
plumage for several
months*

*Distinctive orange
patches on either
side of neck*

*Single egg weighs
10.5 ounces (310 g)*

King Penguin
Aptenodytes forsteri
Females lay a single egg. The parents
take turns to hold it on their feet for
the entire incubation period of about
55 days. Pairs typically breed twice
every three years.

GREBES AND LOONS

Grebes (family Podicipedidae) and loons, or divers (Gaviidae), are highly specialized for an aquatic lifestyle. Grebes live on all continents and habitually dive in lakes and rivers for insect, fish, mollusk, and crustacean prey. Loons hunt mostly fish, which they sometimes dive great depths to catch, and are so adapted for an aquatic lifestyle that they are unable to walk properly on land.

Western Grebe
Aechmophorus occidentalis
The courtship display of this North American species includes both partners pattering on the water surface.

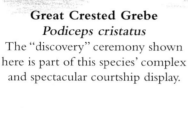

Great Crested Grebe
Podiceps cristatus
The "discovery" ceremony shown here is part of this species' complex and spectacular courtship display.

Chick

Pied-billed Grebe
Podilymbus podiceps
As is typical for the family, adult Pied-billed Grebes carry their small chicks on their back.

Ear tufts are lost in winter

Horned Grebe
Podiceps auritus
Bright orange ear tufts in the breeding season give this species its North American name. In the UK it is called the Slavonian Grebe.

Little Grebe
Tachybaptus ruficollis
During the breeding season this widespread Old World grebe produces distinctive whinnying calls.

Red-throated Loon
Gavia stellata
The nest, lined with vegetation and a few feathers, is built within 18 inches (46 cm) of the margin of a small lake. The female lays two eggs. This is the most common of the five loon species.

Great Northern Loon
Gavia immer
This bird can dive 200 feet (61 m) below the water surface and remain underwater for three minutes.

Black-throated Loon
Gavia arctica
The striking black-and-white throat pattern is lost in winter.

ALBATROSSES, SHEARWATERS, AND GANNETS

The albatrosses, shearwaters, and gannets (families Diomedeidae, Procellariidae, and Sulidae) are the world's most oceanic birds. Shearwaters range over all the world's oceans, while albatrosses are more concentrated in the Southern Hemisphere than the Northern. Both groups take squid, fish, crustaceans, and fisheries waste from the surface or underwater, often swimming in pursuit of prey. The sulids (gannets and boobies) are spectacular plunge-divers.

Dark bill tip of immature Black-browed Albatross

White post-orbital crescent

Light-mantled Sooty Albatross
Phoebetria palpebrata
Breeds in loose colonies on sub-Antarctic islands. A single egg is laid. Fledging takes 140–170 days.

Black-browed Albatross
Thalassarche chlororhynchos
Birds take at least seven years to attain full breeding plumage; this is a sub-adult.

Wandering Albatross
Diomedea epomophora
With the longest wingspan of any bird (up to 11 feet 6 inches, or 3.5 m), it performs extraordinary feats of flight; one bird was logged flying 3,700 miles (5,950 km) in 12 days.

Waved Albatross
Phoebastria irrorata
The amazing courtship display of this Galápagos Islands breeder includes bowing and bill circling and clacking.

Cape Gannet
Morus capensis
Diving almost vertically from 98 feet (30 m), gannets barely slow down when they hit the water in search of fish.

Finely serrated bill to grasp fish

White rump

Cahow
Pterodroma cahow
This nocturnal ground–nesting petrel was thought to be extinct until it was rediscovered in the Bermuda archipelago in 1951.

Peruvian Booby
Sula variegata
A wing-stretching male tries to attract the attention of a flying female at the start of courtship.

Great Shearwater
Puffinus gravis
Breeding is concentrated in the Tristan da Cunha islands in the South Atlantic. Outside the breeding season, these shearwaters migrate north, and then south, around the North Atlantic.

Southern Giant Petrel
Macronectes giganteus
Unlike other petrels, this species will eat carrion and even attack smaller seabirds.

Broad-billed Prion
Pachyptila vittata
This Southern Hemisphere petrel sometimes hydroplanes for food—it flies with its broad, flat bill in the water and filters out food.

HERONS, STORKS, AND CRANES

Being long-legged, these groups of birds look superficially similar but they are not closely related. Herons (family Ardeidae) are wading birds with long or medium-length bills for grabbing aquatic prey. Storks (Ciconiidae) can be seen in fields and grasslands as well as wetlands; they reach their greatest diversity in tropical Africa and Asia. Cranes (Gruidae) are tall and slender, and most are migratory.

Demoiselle Crane
Anthropoides virgo
A long-distance migrant, moving between northern Asia and Africa and South Asia.

Both sexes have golden crown feathers

Black-crowned Crane
Balearica pavonina
This striking bird of sub-Saharan Africa is one of only two crane species to nest in trees.

Black-crowned Night Heron
Nycticorax nycticorax
This widely distributed heron is active at night and around dawn and dusk.

Great Blue Heron
Ardea herodias
The main diet of this New World species is small fish, caught in fresh or salt water.

Bare-throated Tiger Heron
Tigrisoma mexicanum
Waits motionless by the banks of rivers and pools in Central America for frogs, fish, and crabs to come within reach.

Cattle Egret
Bubulcus ibis
This heron's range has increased dramatically due to its mutually advantageous relationship with domesticated cattle.

American Wood Stork
Mycteria americana
A conservation success story in
North America, this stork uses a
"grope-feeding" technique in water
6–10 inches (15–25 cm) deep.

Pink feet

*Bill grows up to
13 inches (33 cm) long*

Marabou Stork
Leptoptilos crumeniferus
This massive African species
may weigh 20 pounds (9 kg).

African Open-bill Stork
Anastomus lamelligerus
This stork has a diet of
aquatic snails and mussels.

White Stork
Ciconia ciconia
Breeds in Europe, North Africa, and
Central Asia, and winters in sub-
Saharan Africa and South Asia.

IBISES, SPOONBILLS, AND FLAMINGOS

Ibises and spoonbills (family Threskiornithidae) feed by feel more than sight. Ibises use their long bills to probe in shallow water and soft mud. Spoonbills swing their open bills from side to side in water. Flamingos (family Phoenicopteridae) are not closely related. They feed on microscopic blue-green algae in alkaline salt lakes or small invertebrates and crustaceans.

James' Flamingo
Phoenicoparrus jamesi
A species living in and around high-altitude lakes (up to 15,980 feet, 4,870 m).

Chilean Flamingo
Phoenicopterus chilensis
This bird, here shown stretching one wing, lives in temperate South America.

Lesser Flamingo
Phoeniconaias minor
The most plentiful flamingo has adapted to thrive in the extremely salty lakes of the African Rift Valley.

Only adults have vivid red plumage

Scarlet Ibis
Eudocimus ruber
Lives at low altitudes in South America, with huge concentrations in wetlands such as the Llanos, in northern Venezuela.

Eurasian Spoonbill
Platalea leucorodia
Its bill is a highly specialized organ for filter-feeding in shallow water and mud.

White-faced Ibis
Plegadis chihi
This bird feeds and breeds in both freshwater and saltwater marshes in North and South America.

Typical downcurved ibis bill

Hadada Ibis
Bostrychia hagedash
A resident of open grasslands, savanna, and wetlands in sub-Saharan Africa.

Spatulate bill

Roseate Spoonbill
Ajaia ajaja
As with flamingos, the plumage's pink color is a result of eating carotenoid pigment found in their diet of crustaceans and algae.

Glossy Ibis
Plegadis falcinellus
This, the world's most widely distributed ibis, feeds in very shallow water.

SWANS AND GEESE

Along with ducks, swans and geese form the large family Anatidae.
They appear on every continent except Antarctica and fill every
aquatic niche from inshore oceanic water to lowland swamps,
and from fast-flowing mountain streams to tundra pools. Many
species breed at high latitudes in the Northern Hemisphere
and fly south in fall when temperatures fall below freezing.

Whooper Swan
Cygnus cygnus
Breeds in Eurasian taiga
and winters farther south
and west. This and Mute
Swan *(Cygnus olor)* are
the largest members
of the family.

Bar-headed Goose
Anser indicus
When migrating to and
from Central Asian
breeding grounds, birds
cross the Himalayas at up
to 23,920 feet (7,290 m).

Black-necked Swan
Cygnus melanocorypha
This swan lives on the margins of
freshwater marshes, lagoons, and lakes
in southern South America.

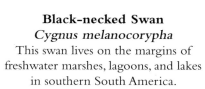

Red-breasted Goose
Branta ruficollis
This beautifully marked, but
endangered, goose nests on tundra on
just three Russian peninsulas. Most birds
winter just west of the Black Sea.

Emperor Goose
Chen canagicus
Almost the entire population winters on
the Aleutian Islands after breeding in
Kamchatka, Russia, and mainland Alaska.

Greylag Goose
Anser anser
The largest of the gray geese
in the genus *Anser*, this species
has expanded its breeding
range in recent times.

Magpie Goose
Anseranas semipalmata
A resident breeding species in
northern Australia and southern
New Guinea.

*Lowered head
and neck of an
aggressive male*

Canada Goose
Branta canadensis
A native of North America, this noisy
goose has been introduced to parts of
Europe, notably the United Kingdom.

Hawaiian Goose
Branta sandvicensis
Endemic to the Hawaiian Islands, this goose was
reduced to just 30 or so wild individuals in the mid-
20th century. Successful conservation measures resulted
in the Hawaiian population rising to 2,000 by 2011.

DUCKS

There are several tribes of duck species, the largest being the surface-feeding, or dabbling, ducks (tribe Anatini). Most are ground-nesters, although Wood Duck and Mandarin Duck are exceptions. The shelducks form another tribe (Tadornini), including the misnamed Egyptian Goose. Whistling ducks make up yet another tribe (Dendrocygnini).

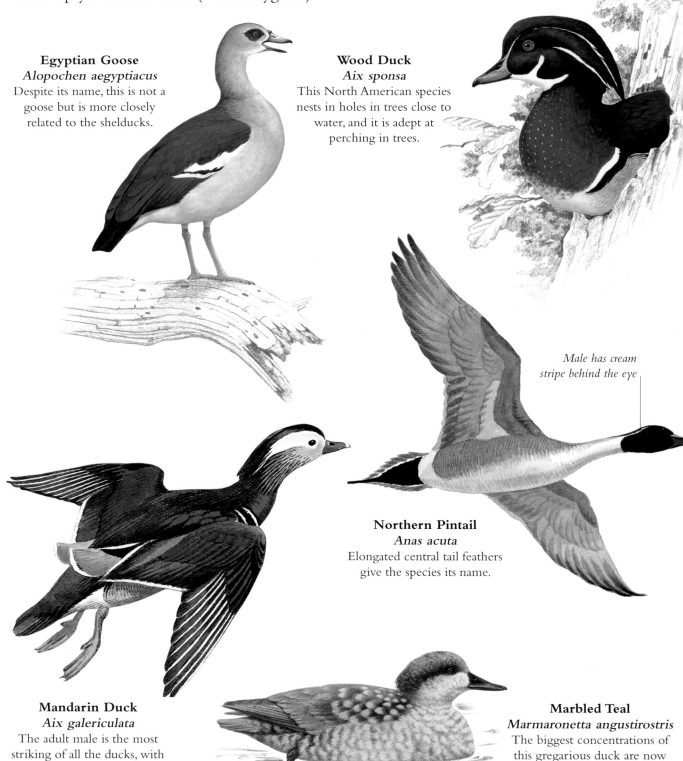

Egyptian Goose
Alopochen aegyptiacus
Despite its name, this is not a goose but is more closely related to the shelducks.

Wood Duck
Aix sponsa
This North American species nests in holes in trees close to water, and it is adept at perching in trees.

Male has cream stripe behind the eye

Northern Pintail
Anas acuta
Elongated central tail feathers give the species its name.

Mandarin Duck
Aix galericulata
The adult male is the most striking of all the ducks, with two orange "sails" on its back.

Marbled Teal
Marmaronetta angustirostris
The biggest concentrations of this gregarious duck are now known to be in southern Iraq.

White-faced Whistling Duck
Dendrocygna viduata
Being relatively long-legged, whistling ducks are good walkers. They are widely distributed in tropical South America and sub-Saharan Africa.

Some dabbling ducks
1. **American Wigeon,** *Anas americana*
2. **Ruddy Shelduck,** *Tadorna ferruginea*
3. **Mallard,** *Anas platyrhynchos*

Common Shelduck
Tadorna tadorna
In late summer flocks of more than 200,000 molting birds congregate in the Wadden Sea, off the coast of the Netherlands.

VULTURES AND SECRETARYBIRD

Vultures spend much of their time soaring high on open wings as they search for food, which for most species is carrion. Although they look superficially similar, the New World vultures (family Cathartidae) and Old World vultures (Accipitridae) are not closely related. The Secretarybird of sub-Saharan Africa is in its own family (Sagittariidae), as befits a bird with a unique hunting strategy.

Wingspan up to 10 feet 6 inches (3.2 m)

Black Vulture
Coragyps atratus
This common New World vulture finds carrion by sight or by following *Cathartes* vultures, which can smell rotting meat.

Andean Condor
Vultur gryphus
A scarce bird of the Andes Mountains, this bird nests on rocky ledges at altitudes up to 16,000 feet (4,877 m).

White rump

Asian White-backed Vulture
Gyps bengalensis
Once described as the most abundant large bird of prey in the world, this Old World vulture is now critically endangered. Its decline is attributed to the use of the drug diclofenac to treat cattle, the carcasses of which are eaten by vultures.

Cinereous Vulture
Aegypius monachus
This Old World vulture raises a single young bird each year. Here, a parent carries water in its bill to its chick.

Palm-nut Vulture
Gypohierax angolensis
This African species eats mostly
fruits, especially those of oil and
raffia palms.

Legs outstretched

Secretarybird
Sagittarius serpentarius
Looking like a cross between a raptor and a
stork (above), this bird of African savannas
flies with its neck and legs outstretched.
It has a unique hunting strategy, stalking
reptiles, rodents, and large invertebrates
on the ground (below).

Long legs

King Vulture
Sarcoramphus papa
A resident of dense tropical forests, this
New World vulture eats anything from
cattle carcasses to dead lizards and
beached fish.

FALCONS

The true falcons (family Falconidae) are stocky, fast-flying birds with long, pointed wings. They often kill other birds in full flight. The falconets and pygmy-falcons are smaller— Black-thighed Falconet, for example (not illustrated), is only 6 inches (15 cm) long. They hunt insects, small reptiles, and small birds. Caracaras' diet is mostly carrion.

Two small falcons
Male **American Kestrel**, *Falco sparverius* (below left), a common small falcon of the Americas; and male **Common Kestrel**, *Falco tinnunculus*, its counterpart in Eurasia.

Southern Crested Caracara
Polyborus plancus
A large, long-legged bird of open country, it eats mostly carrion, with some insects, small vertebrates, and fruit.

Strong, hooked bill

Two large falcons
The **Peregrine**, *Falco peregrinus* (above left), is the most cosmopolitan falcon, found in every continent. In contrast, the **Aplomado Falcon**, *Falco femoralis* (above right), breeds only in South and Central America.

Red-footed Falcon
Falco vespertinus
This Eurasian raptor hovers, searching the ground below, then makes a short, steep dive to seize its prey.

Sharp talons grab prey

Pygmy Falcon
Polihierax semitorquatus
Just 8 inches (20 cm) long, this is the smallest raptor on the African continent.

Gyrfalcon
Falco rusticolus
This is the biggest falcon: large females weigh up to 4.6 pounds (2.1 kg), 35 per cent heavier than female Peregrines.

Barred Forest Falcon
Micrastur ruficollis
A species that hunts by perching quietly on a branch and then waiting for its prey—small birds, mammals, lizards, and snakes—to appear.

Mauritius Kestrel
Falco punctatus
Living only on the Indian Ocean island of Mauritius, the numbers of this small falcon have recovered from just four wild birds in 1974 to an estimated 400 in 2012.

Laughing Falcon
Herpetotheres cachinnans
This South and Central American falcon has a striking face mask and an equally striking laughing call.

HAWKS AND EAGLES

There are four main groups in the family Accipitridae: Old World vultures; birds in the genus *Accipiter*, often called accipiters; those in the genus *Buteo* (hawks, or buzzards in the Old World); and true eagles. Accipiters are small to medium-sized hunters with short, rounded wings and long tails. Buteos are medium-sized to large birds with broad wings. True eagles have long, broad wings; some are very large birds.

Contrasting hawks
The **Eastern Chanting Goshawk,** *Melierax poliopterus* (right), is on top of a termite mound; termites form a major part of the species' diet. The **Eurasian Sparrowhawk,** *Accipiter nisus* (below), eats mostly small birds.

Long-tailed Hawk
Urotriorchis macrourus
Its tail makes up more than half the length of this African rainforest raptor.

European Honey-buzzard
Pernis apivorus
A long-distance migrant whose diet is primarily the larvae of wasps and bees.

Black-mantled Sparrowhawk
Accipiter melanochlamys
This forest raptor of New Guinea has just caught a small bird.

Swainson's Hawk
Buteo swainsoni
Long-distance migrants between North and South America, these hawks sometimes form flocks tens of thousands strong in fall.

Bald Eagle
Haliaeetus leucocephalus
Since a low point in the 1960s, the population of this national symbol of the United States has recovered dramatically.

Verreaux's Eagle
Aquila verreauxii
Hyraxes make up more than 60 per cent of this eagle's diet.

Ornate Hawk-eagle
Spizaetus ornatus
Deforestation in its native South America is a major threat to this impressive bird of prey (left).

White 'hood'

Long-legged Buzzard
Buteo rufinus
One of about 30 species in the genus *Buteo*, characterized by their large size, broad wings, and opportunistic feeding behavior.

Spanish Imperial Eagle
Aquila adalberti
Endemic to Iberia, it has been brought back from the brink of extinction.

Swallow-tailed Kite
Elanoides forficatus
An incredibly graceful aerial hunter with swept-back wings and a forked tail.

PHEASANTS, QUAILS, AND PARTRIDGES

Pheasants, quails, and partridges (family Phasianidae) often have very striking plumage, especially the males, epitomized by the Blue Peafowl's extravagant tail. Most members of the family are rotund, heavy birds with rounded wings and short legs. They range in size from the large Blue Peafowl to the 6-inch (15 cm) Blue Quail. Red Junglefowl is the ancestor of the domestic chicken.

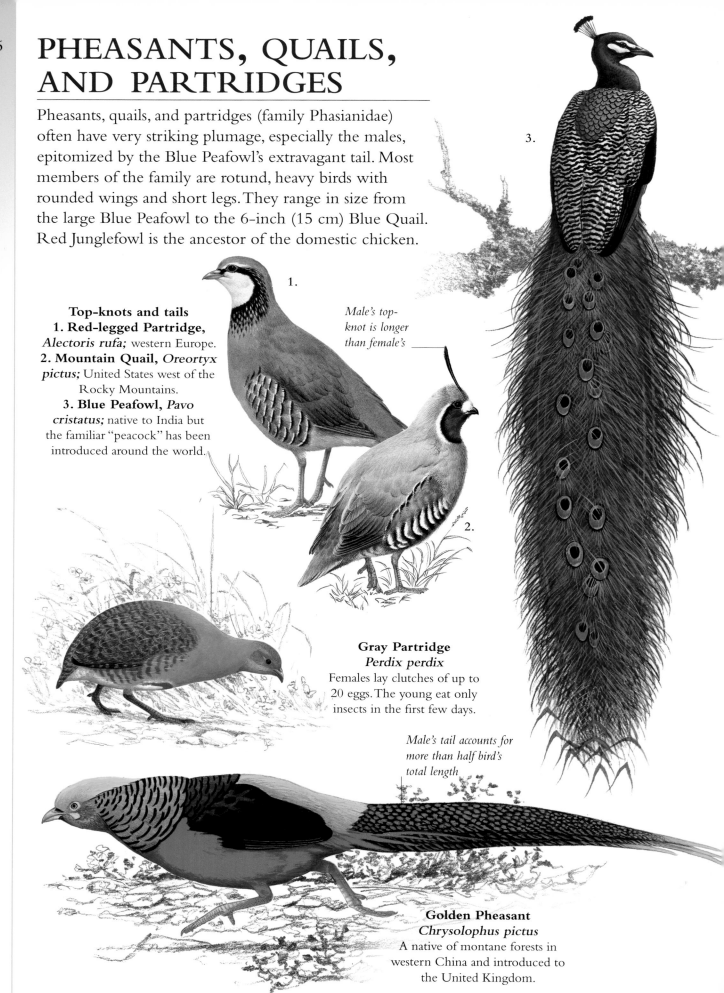

Top-knots and tails
1. Red-legged Partridge, *Alectoris rufa;* western Europe.
2. Mountain Quail, *Oreortyx pictus;* United States west of the Rocky Mountains.
3. Blue Peafowl, *Pavo cristatus;* native to India but the familiar "peacock" has been introduced around the world.

Male's top-knot is longer than female's

Gray Partridge
Perdix perdix
Females lay clutches of up to 20 eggs. The young eat only insects in the first few days.

Male's tail accounts for more than half bird's total length

Golden Pheasant
Chrysolophus pictus
A native of montane forests in western China and introduced to the United Kingdom.

Ring-necked Pheasant
Phasianus colchicus
Native to Asia, this bird has been introduced to most parts of the world for captive-breeding.

Red Junglefowl
Gallus gallus
This is the wild Asian ancestor of the domestic chicken.

Lady Amherst's Pheasant
Chrysolophus amherstiae
This bird's preferred habitat in its native China is dense, dark forest with a thick understory.

Northern Bobwhite, *Colinus virginianus* (above left), is a sedentary quail of eastern North America, while **Common Quail,** *Coturnix coturnix* (above right), is a long-distance migrant between Eurasia and Africa/South Asia.

Chukar
Alectoris chukar
Likes open, rocky hillsides with some grass and scrubby cover in southern Europe and Central Asia.

GROUSE, GUINEAFOWL, AND BUSTARDS

The grouse (family Tetraonidae) are plump, short-legged birds of forests, grasslands, and tundra in the Northern Hemisphere. The six species of guineafowl (Numididae) are terrestrial birds of savanna or forest in sub-Saharan Africa. Bustards (Otididae) are also terrestrial, but they are long-legged and exclusively species of open country in Eurasia, Africa, and Australasia.

Some white winter plumage remains

Willow Ptarmigan
Lagopus lagopus
This bird is molting from its white winter plumage to its rusty-red and white summer feathers.

Sage Grouse
Centrocercus urophasianus
This male is displaying at a communal courtship site, or lek.

Spruce Grouse
Dendragapus canadensis
In the harsh Canadian winter this grouse survives largely on a diet of pine needles.

Sharp-tailed Grouse
Tympanuchus cupido
A bird of the North American prairies, this individual is displaying the pointed tail for which it is named.

Black ruff shows this is a male in breeding plumage

Houbara Bustard
Chlamydotis undulata
A resident of sandy and stony semi-deserts in North Africa, the Middle East, and Central Asia, its diet is invertebrates, small vertebrates, and green shoots.

Red-crested Bustard
Eupodotis ruficrista
A common bird on the savannas of sub-Saharan Africa.

Lesser Florican
Sypheotides indica
A bird of dry Indian grasslands, this bustard is endangered and still decreasing as hunting and habitat change take their toll.

Guineafowl
Crested Guineafowl,
Guttera pucherani, above;
a bird of African scrub forest.
Vulturine Guineafowl,
Acryllium vulturinum,
right; the species is so named because its head is suppposed to resemble that of an Old World vulture.

Great Bustard
Otis tarda
Males weigh up to 40 pounds (18 kg), making them the heaviest of all flying birds. This male is performing its courtship display.

SANDPIPERS, SNIPES, AVOCETS, AND STILTS

The avocets and stilts (family Recurvirostridae) make up a small group of long-legged waders found in tropical and temperate regions. Sandpipers and snipes in the much larger family Scolopacidae have long legs, a short tail, and often long legs. They exhibit a large range of bill structures, reflecting dietary specializations, and most migrate to and from high-latitude breeding areas.

Common Snipe
Gallinago gallinago
During display flights a male snipe's outer tail feathers flutter as the bird dives, making a distinctive "drumming" sound.

Legs trail in flight

Eurasian Avocet
Recurvirostra avosetta
This noisy wader uses its upturned bill to filter the upper silt layers in shallow coastal pools for small crustaceans and worms.

Dunlin
Calidris alpina
Nesting on moist boggy ground with tussock tundra in the Arctic, Dunlin desert the breeding areas in autumn to form feeding flocks—sometimes thousands strong—on estuaries farther south.

Black-winged Stilt
Himantopus himantopus
This elegant stilt's legs are longer in proportion to the remainder of the body than in any other birds apart from flamingos.

Common Sandpiper
Tringa hypoleucos
When disturbed, this sandpiper of
upland rivers and lakes typically
delivers a three-note call and flies
away on stiff wings.

Spoon-billed Sandpiper
Eurynorhynchus pygmeus
The spatulate bill of this critically
endangered Siberian breeder is unique
among the waders. Fewer than 250 of
these birds survive in the wild.

Eurasian Curlew
Numenius arquata
This large shorebird uses its long,
downcurved bill to probe in mud
for crustaceans and mollusks.

*The female's
bill is even
longer than
the male's*

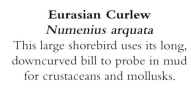

Sanderling
Calidris alba
This long-distance migrant
breeds in the Arctic, as close to
the North Pole as 82°N. The
bird illustrated is in non-
breeding plumage.

Bar-tailed Godwit
Limosa lapponica
Individuals returning from New Zealand
to breeding grounds in Siberia undertake
the longest non-stop migration flight of
any bird: 5,950 miles (9,575 km).

GULLS AND TERNS

Although gulls (family Laridae) have a worldwide distribution, they are more common in the Northern Hemisphere, where they survive even in the harshest environments. The Ivory Gull, a noted scavenger, lives in the high Arctic. Some gulls breed far from water, but others never venture away from the ocean except to breed. Terns (Sternidae) are wonderfully graceful flyers with long, tapering wings and often a longish, forked tail. Many have a bright red or yellow bill.

Caspian Tern
Sterna caspia
The world's largest tern breeds on most continents. It has a wingspan of at least 51 inches (130 cm).

Typical long, narrow wings

Large-billed Tern
Phaetusa simplex
Lives by rivers and freshwater lakes in South America.

White forehead

Sooty Tern
Sterna fuscata
This species nests on tropical islands and ranges through all the world's tropical oceans. It is seldom seen near land except when breeding.

Delicate bill

Three tropical terns
1. **Blue-gray Noddy,** *Procelsterna cerulea:* nests on many islands in the Pacific Ocean.
2. **Lesser Noddy,** *Anous tenuirostris:* breeds on islands and coastlines around the Indian Ocean.
3. **White Tern,** *Gygis alba:* lays its egg on the thin, bare branch of a tree.

1.

2.

3.

Arctic Tern
Sterna paradisaea
These graceful fliers are renowned for their record-breaking migration flights between winter quarters in the Southern Ocean and breeding colonies in the Arctic.

Black Tern
Chlidonias niger
This is one of the "marsh terns," which breed in freshwater wetlands. The birds are much more seafaring outside the breeding season, however. This illustration shows a juvenile.

Black-legged Kittiwake
Rissa tridactyla
The juvenile plumage of this oceanic gull is distinctive, with a black "W" on the upper wings. Adults have plain gray wings.

Great Black-backed Gull
Larus marinus
The largest of all the gulls. This individual in first-winter plumage is scavenging on a dead Razorbill.

Powerful bill

AUKS AND JAEGERS

AUKS AND JAEGERS

Auks are among the commonest seabirds in the Northern Hemisphere. There are 23 species in the family Alcidae, all of which are good swimmers, adept at pursuing prey underwater. They mostly exhibit black and white plumage but have a wide range of bill structures, reflecting adaptations for different diets. The jaegers and skuas (family Stercorariidae) are the pirates of the oceans, forcing other seabirds—including auks—to give up their prey.

Razorbill
Alca torda
This North Atlantic auk has a distinctive stout, deep, round-tipped bill.

Parakeet Auklet
Aethia psittacula
Breeding in rock crevices on the cliffs, slopes, and boulder fields of offshore islands in the North Pacific, this bird often nests close to other auk species.

Multicolored bill

Atlantic Puffin
Fratercula arctica
Puffins swallow their food underwater unless they are feeding young; then they can return to the nest burrow with up to 30 sand eels in their bill.

Japanese Murrelet
Synthliboramphus wumizusume
This bird has just emerged from its nest cavity; it breeds on rocky islands and headlands around Japan.

Arctic Jaeger
Stercorarius parasiticus
Like other skuas, it exhibits
piratical behavior, robbing gulls
and terns of their catches.

Little Auk
Alle alle
This is the most numerous bird in
the Svalbard archipelago, in the
Arctic Ocean, where there are
more than 200 colonies.

*Twisted central
tail feathers*

White flash in wing

Pomarine Jaeger
Stercorarius pomarinus
Breeds on tundra in northern Alaska,
Canada, and Russia; winters in
tropical oceanic waters.

Great Skua
Catharacta skua
As well as being piratical, this skua
directly attacks and kills other
seabirds, including auks and even
large gulls.

Black Guillemot
Cepphus grylle
Unlike other auks, in the breeding
season this species prefers to forage
in shallow near-shore waters.

PARROTS, LORIES, AND COCKATOOS

There are at least 356 species of parrots and their allies (families Psittacidae) in 80 genera. Native to the tropics and temperate regions of the Southern Hemisphere, these vocal birds have long been popular as pets. Most species are predominantly green, with patches of bright red, yellow, or blue. Others are blue, yellow, or white. Most are vegetarians, though carrion-eating Keas in New Zealand are an exception.

Tricolored underwing

Rainbow Lorikeet
Trichoglossus haematodus
Often seen in loud, fast-moving flocks and at communal roosts in its native Australia.

Hyacinth Macaw
Anodorhynchus hyacinthinus
The largest flying parrot is 39 inches (1 m) long. This endangered South American species has a population of fewer than 6,500.

Very long tail

Red-capped Parrot
Purpureicephalus spurius
This parrot lives in southwest Australia where it feeds mostly on the seeds of eucalypts, insects, and orchard fruits.

Eclectus Parrot
Eclectus roratus
Males of this species are bright emerald green, but females (pictured) are bright red and purplish-blue.

Kea
Nestor notabilis
Native to the mountains of New Zealand's South Island, this parrot includes carrion in its diet.

Night Parrot
Pezoporus occidentalis
A combination of its nocturnal lifestyle and extreme rarity means this Australian species is rarely seen.

Three cockatoos
1. Yellow–tailed Black Cockatoo, *Calyptorhynchus funereus.*
2. Galah, *Eolophus roseicapillus.*
3. Palm Cockatoo, *Probosciger aterrimus.*

1.

2.

3.

Crimson Rosella
Platycercus elegans
This handsome species is native to eastern Australia. The males are a little larger than the females.

OWLS

Owls are characterized by an upright stance, a short tail, and a large head. A dense covering of feathers gives them a neckless appearance. There are two families: true owls (family Strigidae), and barn and bay owls (Tytonidae). Owls live on every continent apart from Antarctica. Most are arboreal but there are scrub, grassland, and even desert species. Most, but not all, hunt at night. Size varies considerably: a female Blakiston's Fish Owl weighs more than 100 times an Elf Owl.

Barking Owl
Ninox connivens
Its calls sound like a barking dog;
males and females sometimes
perform duets.

Spotted Wood Owl
Strix seloputo
A Southeast Asian
species of the "earless"
genus *Strix*.

"Spectacles"

Spectacled Owl
Pulsatrix perspicillata
The largest owl in its favored
old-growth rain forest in
South America, it sometimes
takes prey heavier than itself.

Pel's Fishing Owl
Scotopelia peli
A native of sub-Saharan Africa, this
species takes fish as large as
4.4 pounds (2 kg) from near the
surface of lakes and rivers.

*Long, partly
unfeathered legs*

Boreal Owl
Aegolius funereus
Typical habitat for this owl is the dense coniferous forest belt (taiga) that stretches across northern North America and Eurasia. It also lives in mountain ranges such as the Alps and Rockies.

White-faced Scops Owl
Otus leucotis
When confronted by a larger animal, it pulls its feathers in, elongates its body, and narrows its eyes to camouflage itself.

Elf Owl
Micrathene whitneyi
A tiny species, weighing just 1.4 ounces (40 g), the Elf Owl predates moths and other insects in Mexico and the southwestern United States.

Oriental Bay Owl
Phodilus badius
This Southeast Asian forest species has an angular facial disk with dark vertical markings.

Malaysian Eagle Owl
Bubo sumatranus
A Southeast Asian forest species with extraordinarily long ear tufts.

SWALLOWS AND SWIFTS

Swallows and martins make up a cosmopolitan family (Hirundinidae) of graceful aerial feeders, some of which are long-distance migrants. Barn Swallow is one of the world's most successful bird species, breeding or visiting every continent. If anything, swifts (Apodidae) are even more aerial, even mating and sleeping on the wing. Neither they nor the four species of Asiatic/Australasian treeswifts (Hemiprocnidae) are closely related to swallows.

Southern Rough-winged Swallow
Stelgidopteryx ruficollis
A bird of open areas and forest clearings in Central and South America.

Very long tail streamers

Blue Swallow
Hirundo atrocaerulea
A migrant, breeding in Uganda and spending the winter in Zambia, Zimbabwe, and South Africa.

Tree Swallow
Tachycineta bicolor
Highly gregarious outside the breeding season, a flock in Louisiana, United States, in December 2009 was estimated to contain more than 1 million birds.

NA

Bank Martin
Riparia riparia
This widely distributed
martin nests in holes in
sandy banks and cliffs.

*Long, scythe-
shaped wings*

Common Swift
Apus apus
Swifts do most things on
the wing, including
mating (illustrated here)
and sleeping.

Indian Swiftlet
Aerodramus unicolor
The genus *Aerodramus* contains at
least 28 species of small swifts
called swiftlets.

Resident and migrant swifts
African Palm Swifts, *Cypsiurus*
parvus (left), are widespread residents
of sub-Saharan Africa. In contrast,
most **Alpine Swifts,** *Tachymarptis*
melba (right), breed in a band from
Portugal to Nepal and in South Africa,
but migrate to winter quarters in
tropical Africa.

Crested Treeswift
Hemiprocne coronata
A common resident in South
Asia. Only adult males have
the orange cheek flash.

HUMMINGBIRDS

There are well over 300 species of hummingbirds (family Trochilidae) in the New World. They range from southern Argentina to southern Alaska, but the greatest diversity of species is in Colombia (more than 160 species). Some 90 per cent of a hummingbird's diet is nectar, and consequently the birds are found where there are nectar-producing flowers, from sea level to the snowline in the Andes. High-latitude breeders are migratory.

Ruby-throated Hummingbird
Archilochus colubris
A long-distance migrant, this species breeds in the United States and Canada, and winters from Mexico south to Panama.

Chestnut-bellied Hummingbird
Amazilia castaneiventris
This endangered species lives in dry valleys in Colombia. The illustrated bird is a male.

Giant Hummingbird
Patagona gigas
This bird lives on mountain slopes in Argentina, Chile, Bolivia, Peru, Ecuador, and Colombia.

White forehead and cap

Reddish Hermit
Phaethornis ruber
Like most hermits, this species feeds on the nectar of *Heliconia* flowers. Reddish Hermits live in humid forests in the Amazon Basin.

Snowcap
Microchera albocoronata
A resident mostly of lowland humid forests in Panama, Costa Rica, Nicaragua, and Honduras.

Ruby-topaz Hummingbird
Chrysolampis mosquitus
A resident of open and cultivated country in northern South America.

Tail reaches 9 inches (22 cm) in length

Scale-throated Hermit
Phaethornis eurynome
A resident of the Atlantic forests of Brazil, Paraguay, and Argentina.

Red-tailed Comet
Sappho sparganura
Red-tailed Comet lives in montane scrub, forest, and grassland in Bolivia and Argentina.

Bill allows access to nectar in Heliconia flowers

Bearded Helmetcrest
Oxypogon guerinii
Favored habitat is montane scrub, above the tree line, in Colombia and Venezuela.

White-tipped Sicklebill
Eutoxeres aquila
The White-tipped Sicklebill lives in humid lowland or montane forests in Peru, Ecuador, Colombia, Panama, and Costa Rica.

Sword-billed Hummingbird
Ensifera ensifera
This species lives in montane forest in the Andes in Bolivia, Peru, Ecuador, and Venezuela.

Fiery-tailed Awlbill
Avocettula recurvirostris
This hummingbird lives in lowland humid forest in the Amazon Basin.

OSPREY AND KINGFISHERS

Ospreys (family Pandionidae) and many of the kingfisher species (Alcedinidae) share hunting behaviors—taking fish from lakes, rivers, and the sea. The 86 kingfisher species have adapted for life in most environments, from rain forests to dry plains, and from riverbanks to mangroves. Many are brightly colored.

Dagger-like bill of a fish-catching species

Pied Kingfisher
Ceyx rudis
One of several species that are able to hover over their prey before diving from a height of up to 39 feet (12 m).

Osprey
Pandion haliaetus
The third toe of this fish-catching raptor can be rotated to provide a better grip on slippery fish.

Sharp spines under toes

THE BILLS OF KINGFISHERS

Kingfishers' bills demonstrate a wide range of adaptations for different diets. The Shovel-billed Kingfisher's short, conical bill is ideal for taking earthworms from the ground. A Laughing Kookaburra can take lizards with its strong beak. The long, thin bill of a Small Blue Kingfisher is characteristic of a fishing species.

Short and conical

1.

Very stout

2.

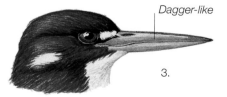
Dagger-like

3.

1. **Shovel-billed Kookaburra**, *Clytoceyx rex*
2. **Laughing Kookaburra**, *Dacelo novaeguineae*
3. **Small Blue Kingfisher**, *Alcedo coerulescens*

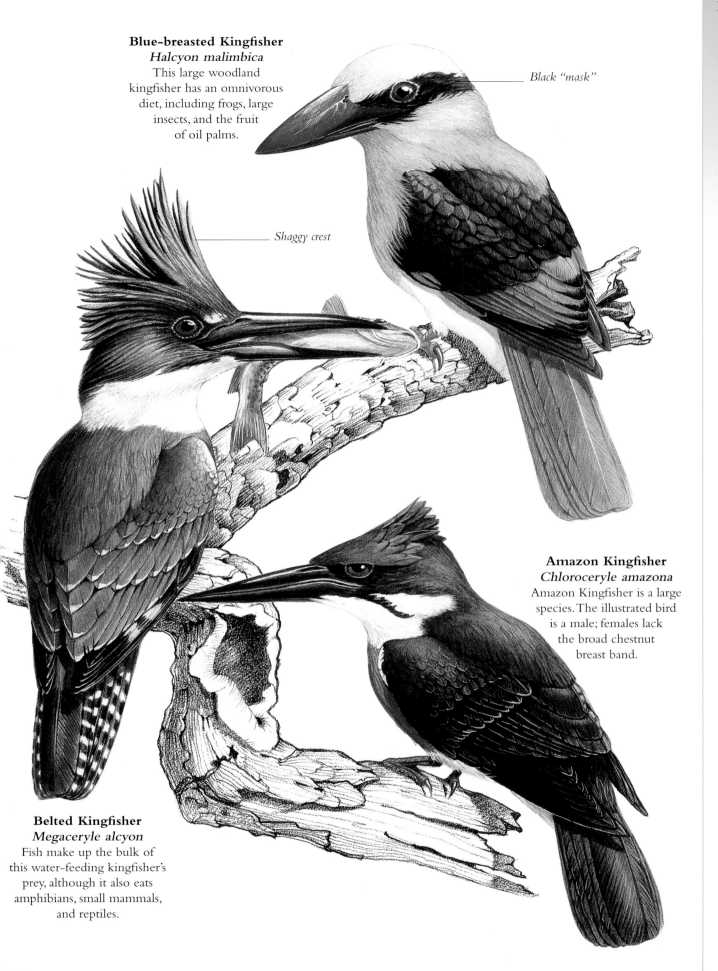

Blue-breasted Kingfisher
Halcyon malimbica
This large woodland kingfisher has an omnivorous diet, including frogs, large insects, and the fruit of oil palms.

Black "mask"

Shaggy crest

Amazon Kingfisher
Chloroceryle amazona
Amazon Kingfisher is a large species. The illustrated bird is a male; females lack the broad chestnut breast band.

Belted Kingfisher
Megaceryle alcyon
Fish make up the bulk of this water-feeding kingfisher's prey, although it also eats amphibians, small mammals, and reptiles.

MOTMOTS, TROGONS, AND BEE-EATERS

The motmots and the much smaller todies (families Momotidae and Todidae) are brightly colored New World forest species. Bee-eaters (Meropidae) also sport vivid colors but are birds of the Old World, where most live in open habitats, although a few prefer rain-forest environments. Trogons (Trogonidae) are predominantly forest species of tropical South America, Africa, and Asia.

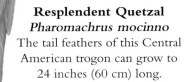

Elongated greater wing coverts

Resplendent Quetzal
Pharomachrus mocinno
The tail feathers of this Central American trogon can grow to 24 inches (60 cm) long.

Blue-crowned Motmot
Momotus momota
This bird often beats a butterfly against a branch to knock its wings off before swallowing the body.

Large head relative to body size

Collared Trogon
Trogon collaris
A resident breeder in semi-arid open forest in much of Central America.

Cuban Tody
Todus multicolor
There are five species of todies on the larger islands of the Caribbean; this species is native to Cuba.

Downcurved bill

Blue-bearded Bee-eater
Nyctyornis athertoni
Forest clearings provide the typical habitat for this South and Southeast Asian bee-eater.

European Bee-eater
Merops apiaster
This long-distance migrant's name is something of a misnomer since it breeds in southwest Asia and southern Africa as well as Europe. The entire population winters in sub-Saharan Africa.

Purple-bearded Bee-eater
Meropogon forsteni
This species' habitat preference is similar to that of Blue-bearded, but Purple-bearded Bee-eater is endemic to the island of Sulawesi, in Indonesia.

Tail streamers are 2.5 inches (6 cm) long

Little Bee-eater
Merops pusillus
A common bird of open country with scattered bushes in sub-Saharan Africa, this species tunnels into sandy banks to make a nest-hole.

TOUCANS AND HORNBILLS

The most prominent feature of toucans (family Ramphastidae) is their large, brightly colored bill, which is used to pluck seeds and berries from twigs too flimsy to bear the birds' weight. Similarities between them and the unrelated Old World hornbills (Bucerotidae) can be explained by convergent evolution.

Emerald Toucanet
Aulacorhynchus prasinus
Small flocks of these toucanets fly through humid forests with rapid, direct flight.

Russet rump

Saffron Toucanet
Baillonius bailloni
The caged-bird trade and forest destruction have led to a decline in this the numbers of this species.

Berry carried in bill

1.

2.

3.

Ramphastos and **Andigena**
1. **Toco Toucan**, *Ramphastos toco:* semi-open habitats in southern South America.
2. **Black-billed Mountain-toucan**, *Andigena nigrirostris:* slopes of northern Andes above 1,200 m (3,937 ft).
3. **Chestnut-mandibled Toucan**, *Ramphastos swainsonii:* forests in Central America and northern South America.

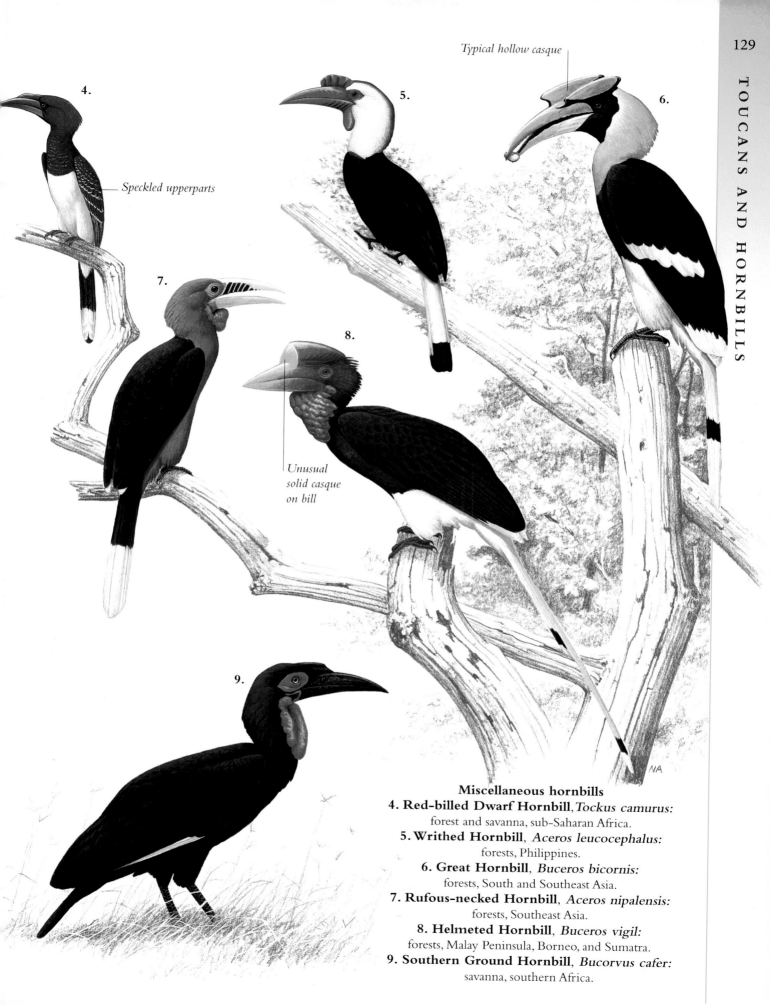

Typical hollow casque

Speckled upperparts

Unusual solid casque on bill

4.

5.

6.

7.

8.

9.

NA

Miscellaneous hornbills

4. Red-billed Dwarf Hornbill, *Tockus camurus*:
forest and savanna, sub–Saharan Africa.

5. Writhed Hornbill, *Aceros leucocephalus*:
forests, Philippines.

6. Great Hornbill, *Buceros bicornis*:
forests, South and Southeast Asia.

7. Rufous-necked Hornbill, *Aceros nipalensis*:
forests, Southeast Asia.

8. Helmeted Hornbill, *Buceros vigil*:
forests, Malay Peninsula, Borneo, and Sumatra.

9. Southern Ground Hornbill, *Bucorvus cafer*:
savanna, southern Africa.

JACAMARS AND WOODPECKERS

Jacamars (family Galbulidae) are tropical insectivores of the New World. They are usually solitary birds of forest and forest edge. The large woodpecker family (Picidae) has representatives on every continent apart from Australasia. Woodpeckers are expert climbers, hunt and eat insects hidden under bark or in wood, use drumming to communicate, and excavate nest-holes in trees.

Paradise Jacamar
Galbula dea
Unlike most other jacamars, this species tends to perch high in the canopy, waiting for an insect to fly past.

Miscellaneous woodpeckers
1. **Three-toed Woodpecker**, *Picoides tridactylus:* Eurasia
2. **Northern Flicker**, *Colaptes auratus:* North America
3. **Green Woodpecker**, *Picus viridis:* Eurasia
4. **Great Spotted Woodpecker**, *Dendrocopos major:* Eurasia
5. **Red-headed Woodpecker**, *Melanerpes erythrocephalus:* North America
6. **Eurasian Wryneck**, *Jynx torquilla:* Eurasia and Africa
7. **Olive-backed Three-toed Woodpecker**, *Dinopium rafflesii:* Southeast Asia

Long central tail feathers

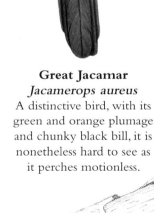

Great Jacamar
Jacamerops aureus
A distinctive bird, with its green and orange plumage and chunky black bill, it is nonetheless hard to see as it perches motionless.

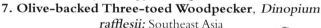

1.

2.

Pileated Woodpecker
Dryocopus pileatus
This is the largest
woodpecker in North
America. Owls and
tree-nesting ducks rely
on the cavities excavated
by this species for their
own nest-holes.

Yellow-bellied Sapsucker
Sphyrapicus varius
The four species of sapsucker drill
holes in trees to feed on the sap
and eat the insects that are
drawn to the sap.

LYREBIRDS, BOWERBIRDS, AND BIRDS OF PARADISE

These three families are not closely related but all exhibit extraordinary courtship displays or rituals and the males sport incredible plumes, tail feathers, or breast shields. Male bowerbirds (Ptilonorhynchidae) build elaborate bowers (stick structures) to impress females. Male lyrebirds (Menuridae) and birds of paradise (Paradisaea) perform extravagant courtship displays.

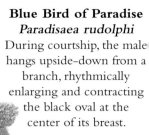

Blue Bird of Paradise
Paradisaea rudolphi
During courtship, the male hangs upside-down from a branch, rhythmically enlarging and contracting the black oval at the center of its breast.

Plumes spread in fan during display

Archbold's Bowerbird
Archboldia papuensis
Males of this New Guinea species collect the plumes of King of Saxony Birds of Paradise to decorate their courtship bower.

Breast shield flared during display

Twelve-wired Bird of Paradise
Seleucidis melanoleuca
Twelve wire filaments emerge from the yellow plumes on the flanks.

Neck mantle

Magnificent Bird of Paradise
Diphyllodes magnificus
The male's plumage features an iridescent green breast shield, two sickle-like tail feathers, and a yellow neck mantle.

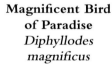

Filament

Superb Lyrebird
Menura novaehollandiae
The male's extraordinary tail has 16 long feathers, which take seven years to develop fully.

**Emperor
Bird of Paradise**
Paradisaea guilielmi
This resident of the hill forests of the Huon Peninsula, New Guinea, hangs upside-down and displays two very long tail wires during courtship.

Tail wire

Magnificent Riflebird
Ptiloris magnificus
During its display the male fully extends its wings and raises its tail, swinging its head from side to side.

CROWS, THRUSHES, AND CHATS

The crows (family Corvidae) are intelligent, opportunist feeders. There are more than 300 species of thrush (Turdidae), including the familiar American Robin. Formerly considered to be thrushes, the chats—including Eurasian Robin—are now included in the Old World flycatchers (Muscicapidae).

Eurasian Jay
Garrulus glandarius
Brighter-plumaged than most crows, this species stores acorns in the fall to feed on when food is scarce in winter.

Eurasian Magpie
Pica pica
A resident through much of Europe, parts of Asia, and northwest Africa.

Long tail feathers

1.

Orange outer tail feathers

2.

3.

Blue Jay
Cyanocitta cristata
A noisy, boisterous, and colorful
resident of the United States
and southern Canada east of
the Rocky Mountains.

Rook
Corvus frugilegus
This Eurasian crow breeds in
large colonies called rookeries.

Common Raven
Corvus corax
The largest corvid has a
reputation for intelligence—and
aggressive behavior.

Miscellaneous thrushes and chats
1. **Eurasian Robin**, *Erithacus rubecula*
2. **Song Thrush**, *Turdus philomelos*
3. **White-browed Robin-chat**,
   Cossypha heuglini
4. **Fieldfare**, *Turdus pilaris*
5. **American Robin**, *Turdus migratorius*

TITS AND BUNTINGS

Two very different families of song birds, the tits (families Paridae and Aegithalidae) live in North America, Eurasia, and Africa. They are chiefly birds of forests and woodlands. In contrast, the buntings and New World sparrows (Emberizidae) are more closely associated with open country, from Arctic tundra and alpine meadows to open woodland in the tropics.

Blue Tit
Parus caeruleus
A common European breeding bird and one that often nests in suburban backyards.

Azure Tit
Parus cyanus
This resident of Eurasian deciduous and mixed forests nests in tree-holes.

Black crest

Yellow-cheeked Tit
Parus spilonotus
A bird of mature forests in Southeast Asia.

Black-eared Bushtit
Psaltriparus minimus melanotis
This southern Mexican subspecies of Bushtit is a member of the long-tailed tit family.

Rufous-bellied Tit
Parus rufiventris
This species forages in the leaf canopy, feeding on insects from under leaves and from bark.

Conical bill

Black-headed Bunting
Emberiza melanocephala
A long-distance migrant, moving seasonally between southeast Europe and South Asia.

Corn Bunting
Emberiza calandra
The song of this Eurasian farmland bunting has been likened to a bunch of keys being jangled.

Heavy streaking on upperparts

White-throated Sparrow
Zonotrichia albicollis
This sweet songster breeds in Canada and New England, wintering in the southern United States.

LARKS AND FINCHES

The 80 or so different kinds of larks (family Alaudidae) are generally birds of open countryside. While lark biodiversity is greatest in arid regions of Africa, there are also larks on Arctic tundra and montane grasslands. Finches (Carduelidae) are even more diverse, inhabiting forest, woodland, scrubby country, and grasslands on every continent except Australasia and Antarctica.

Black "horn" feathers on head

Horned Lark
Eremophila alpestris
This bird breeds across much of North America, in Central Asia, and at high latitudes in Eurasia.

Fischer's Sparrow-lark
Eremopterix leucopareia
This bird of sub-Saharan African grasslands is named for the German explorer Gustav Fischer.

Crossed tips of mandibles

Red Crossbill
Loxia curvirostra
Crossbills can prize the scales off pine cones with the unique, crossed mandibles of their bills.

Pine Grosbeak
Pinicola enucleator
When food is scarce, for example if seed crops fail, this species may make unusual migrations southward.

Eurasian Skylark
Alauda arvensis
Celebrated in poems for its
lovely song, delivered in
hovering flight, this lark breeds
across much of Eurasia.

Australasian Lark
Mirafra javanica
This bird of Australian
grasslands has a rich and
varied tinkling song.

Black Lark
*Melanocorypha
yeltoniensis*
This is a bird of open
steppe in Central Asia.

THE BILLS OF FINCHES

The structure of a finch's bill gives strong
clues to its preferred food. For example,
the relatively delicate, but broad-based
bills of Goldfinches and Siskins break
open small seeds; the massive bill of a
Hawfinch crushes cherry stones; and
the crossed mandibles of Two-barred
Crossbills prize open larch cones.

1. **European Goldfinch**, *Carduelis
   carduelis*
2. **Two-barred Crossbill**, *Loxia leucoptera*
3. **Hawfinch**, *Coccothraustes
   coccothraustes*
4. **Siskin**, *Carduelis spinus*

WHAT IS AN AMPHIBIAN?

The class Amphibia comprises more than 5,400 species of frogs, salamanders, and wormlike caecilians. They live on every continent apart from Antarctica. No single structure uniquely defines all amphibians, but they all undergo metamorphosis, the abrupt change from larva to adult. Adult amphibians are carnivores, eating animal prey whole. Fertilization can be internal or external. In most species, females lay eggs in water or damp places, but others are viviparous—they give birth to live young.

▼ SALAMANDER SKELETON

A salamander has a long, flexible body and a long tail, supported by many vertebrae. The forelimbs and hindlimbs of salamanders are of roughly equal length. A salamander's mouth is wide, enabling it to take relatively large prey.

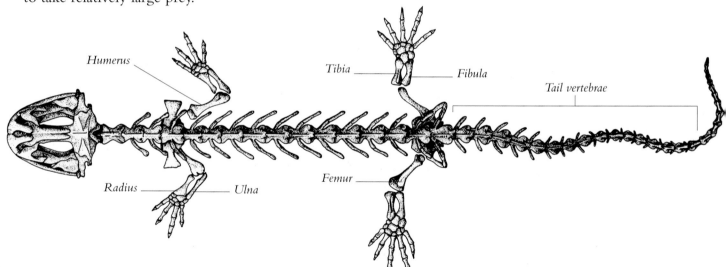

Humerus

Tibia — Fibula

Tail vertebrae

Radius — Ulna

Femur

▶ SKULL

The skull is flattened. In frogs and salamanders it is articulated with the vertebral column by means of two knoblike structures called condyles. Amphibians have pedicellate teeth: the crowns are attached to a narrow pedicle by uncalcified fibrous tissue, allowing the teeth to bend inward.

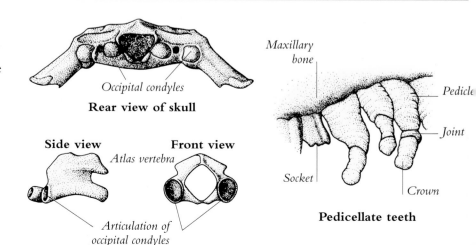

Occipital condyles

Rear view of skull

Side view

Front view

Atlas vertebra

Articulation of occipital condyles

Maxillary bone

Pedicle

Joint

Socket

Crown

Pedicellate teeth

▼ FROG SKELETON

Typical frogs have a short, rigid backbone consisting of a greatly reduced number of vertebrae and no tail. The hindlimbs (made up of the femur and tibio-fibula) of most frogs have become very long, enabling them to leap great distances, and are supported by a massive pelvic girdle. Frogs have larger heads than salamanders, relative to their body size.

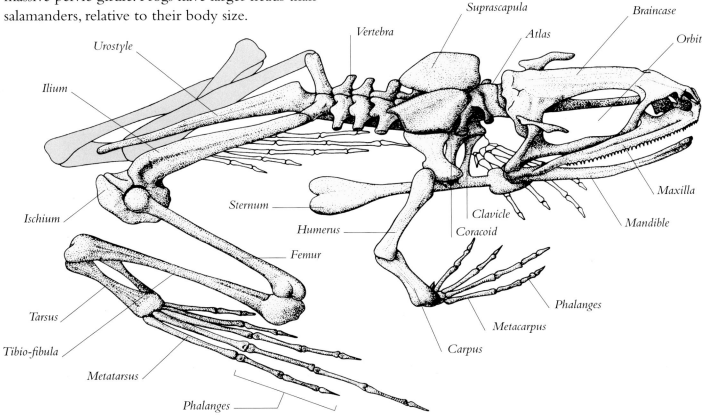

Urostyle

Ilium

Vertebra

Suprascapula

Atlas

Braincase

Orbit

Ischium

Sternum

Humerus

Femur

Clavicle

Coracoid

Maxilla

Mandible

Tarsus

Tibio-fibula

Metatarsus

Phalanges

Carpus

Metacarpus

Phalanges

▶ SKIN STRUCTURE

Amphibians have moist, glandular skin, without scales or true claws. A few frogs, and some legless species called caecilians, have plates of bone (osteoderms) in the skin, as do reptiles. Some frogs and salamanders have clawlike epidermal tips on the toes. Some amphibians have poison glands just below the skin.

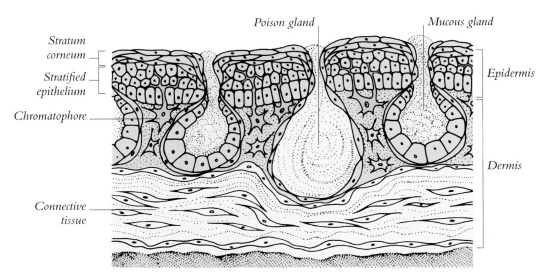

Poison gland

Mucous gland

Stratum corneum

Stratified epithelium

Chromatophore

Connective tissue

Epidermis

Dermis

SALAMANDERS

Salamanders and newts (there are 10 families and more than 400 species) usually have four limbs and a tail, although the sirens have only two limbs. Most salamanders live in the Northern Hemisphere. Some are completely aquatic, but most live in damp places on land.

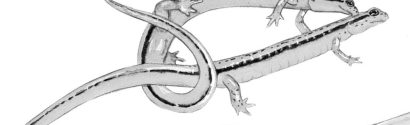

1.

Northern Two-lined Salamander
Eurycea bislineata
This species lives in small rocky streams in forests in Canada and the northeastern United States.

Male clasps female from behind in courtship

Red-cheeked Salamander
Plethodon jordani
Lives in hardwood and coniferous forests in the southeastern United States.

Red-bellied Newt
Taricha rivularis
Found in coastal forests in California and Oregon, United States.

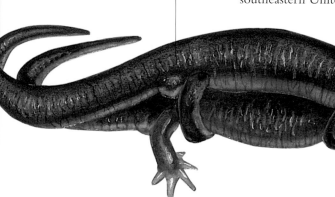

Fire Salamander
Salamandra salamandra
A resident of deciduous forests with small pools or streams in central and southern Europe.

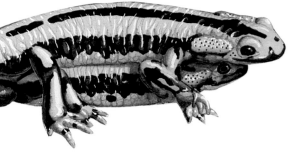

Color gets brighter with age

2.

3.

4.

5.

6.

7.

8.

9.

10.

11.

Forelimb

Male clasps female around the neck in courtship

12.

Miscellaneous salamanders
1. Cocle Salamander, *Bolitoglossa schizodactyla.* **2. Red Salamander**, *Pseudotriton ruber.* **3. Stream Salamander**, *Batrachuperus pinchonii.* **4. Japanese Clawed Salamander**, *Onychodactylus japonicus.* **5. Taliang Knobby Newt**, *Tylototriton taliangensis;* **6. Tiger Salamander**, *Ambystoma tigrinum;* **7. Eastern Newt**, *Notophthalmus viridescens.* **8. Olm**, *Proteus anguinus.* **9. Smooth Newt**, *Triturus vulgaris.* **10. Mudpuppy**, *Necturus maculosus.* **11. Greater Siren**, *Siren lacertina.* **12.** Mating **Eastern Newt**, *Notophthalmus viridescens.*

FROGS AND TOADS

Frogs and toads are the most varied amphibians, with 28 families. They live in most freshwater and terrestrial habitats—even deserts—on every continent apart from Antarctica. The tadpole stage of their life cycle requires fresh water or a damp environment, but this can be a tiny puddle or a patch of damp moss. There are no real differences between frogs and toads.

Oriental Fire-bellied Toad
Bombina orientalis
Its bright colors warn would-be predators of its toxicity; the toxin is secreted through the skin, mostly through the hind legs.

Tubercles on dorsal side

Syrian Spadefoot Toad
Pelobates syriacus
In winter this species hibernates among tree roots or under rocks.

Iberian Midwife Toad
Alytes cisternasii
A male is shown carrying a batch of eggs; he will carry them until they are ready to hatch.

Eggs

"Nose"

Common Spadefoot Toad
Pelobates fuscus
The skin color of this Eurasian species varies according to habitat, location, and gender.

Long-nosed Horned Toad
Megophrys nasuta
A well-camouflaged resident of damp leaf litter in Southeast Asian forests.

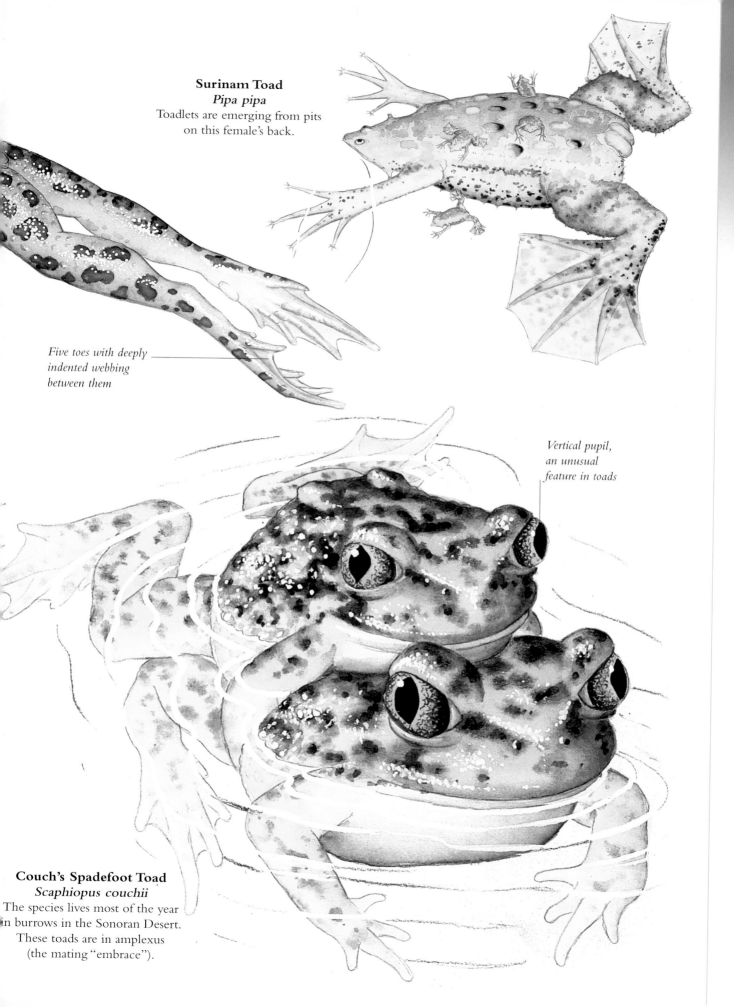

Surinam Toad
Pipa pipa
Toadlets are emerging from pits
on this female's back.

*Five toes with deeply
indented webbing
between them*

*Vertical pupil,
an unusual
feature in toads*

Couch's Spadefoot Toad
Scaphiopus couchii
The species lives most of the year
in burrows in the Sonoran Desert.
These toads are in amplexus
(the mating "embrace").

FROGS AND TOADS

Frogs and toads have diverse reproductive strategies. Almost all species in temperate and arid regions deposit their eggs in ponds where free-swimming tadpoles develop, but many tropical species leave their eggs on vegetation, on the ground, or in excavations. Some frogs lay their eggs on land and there is no tadpole stage. Often, terrestrial eggs are attended by a parent—usually the female—who keeps them moist.

Tadpole

Seychelles Frog
Sooglossus sechellensis
When this frog's tadpoles hatch they climb onto the male's back until they change into froglets.

Large, inflated vocal sac

Cane Toad
Chaunus marinus
Introduced to Australia and other parts of the world to control pests—this species became a pest itself.

Bell's Horned Frog
Ceratophrys ornata
This almost spherical species has a huge mouth and eats anything that will fit in it—including other horned frogs.

Japanese Treefrog
Rhacophorus arboreus
Frogs gather around pools to mate. Eggs are laid in batches of foam suspended from branches overhanging water, and the tadpoles drop into the water.

Waxy Monkey Treefrog
Phyllomedusa sauvagii
Females lay eggs in leaf nests above pools or streams. The males help join the leaves of the nests. When they hatch, the tadpoles drop into the water.

Black-legged Dart Frog
Phyllobates bicolor
The male frog moistens the eggs
until they hatch, then moves the
tadpoles on its back to a
water-filled brooding site.

Asiatic Painted Frog
Kaloula pulchra
During the breeding season,
males of this species often call in
chorus to attract females.

Common Frog
Rana temporaria
Females deposit lumps of
spawn, containing up to
4,500 eggs, into fresh water.

Giant African Bullfrog
Pyxicephalus adspersus
This large frog eats rodents and
other small mammals, reptiles,
amphibians, and even small birds.

WHAT IS A REPTILE?

There are more than 8,000 species of reptiles (class Reptilia), the major groups being turtles, lizards, snakes, and crocodilians. Their most obvious unifying feature is a covering of dry, horny scales.

Reptiles are ectotherms (they do not generate their own body heat) and reproduce by laying shelled eggs on land or by bearing their young alive. They do not have an aquatic larval stage.

▶ LIZARD SCALES

More than half of all reptile species are lizards (order Squamata). Their skin is folded into scales, the outer layer of which is filled with keratin, which greatly reduces water loss and allows many—such as the North African Spiny-tailed Lizard, *Uromastyx acanthinura* (right), to live in very arid habitats. The tail scales on this species have been modified into sharp spines that are used to scare off potential attackers.

Bands of spines on tail

Blunt head

Five digits on each limb

▶ SKIN MODIFICATION

The skin of reptiles shows many modifications. It may be raised up into tubercles, as in the Mountain Horned Agama, *Ceratophora stoddartii*. The skin's epidermis may form crests on the neck, back, or tail, often better developed in the male and perhaps assisting sexual recognition. A good example is the Hump-nosed Lizard, *Lyriocephalus scutatus*.

Tubercles

Crest

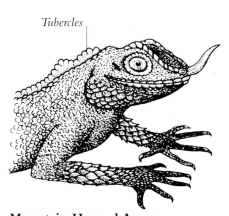

Mountain Horned Agama
Ceratophora stoddarti

Hump-nosed Lizard
Lyriocephalus scutatus

▼ REPTILE SKULLS

Reptiles exhibit a varied range of skeletal design, no more so than with skull structure. Among elements that vary to reflect lifestyle, especially dietary preference, are the length of the mandible, the number and size of the teeth, the number of hinges to give greater or lesser flexibility of jaw articulation, and the size of the eye sockets.

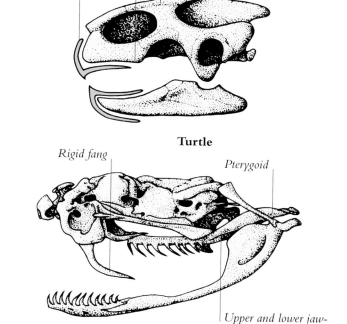

Horny beak

No teeth

Turtle

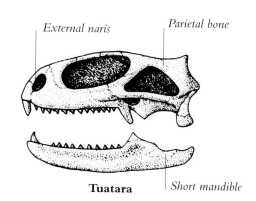

External naris

Parietal bone

Tuatara

Short mandible

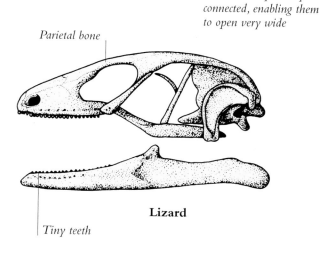

Rigid fang

Pterygoid

Upper and lower jaw-bones are only loosely connected, enabling them to open very wide

Snake

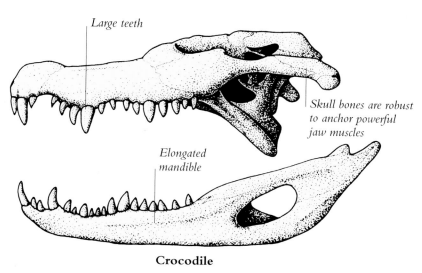

Large teeth

Skull bones are robust to anchor powerful jaw muscles

Elongated mandible

Crocodile

Parietal bone

Tiny teeth

Lizard

► REPTILE EGG

The partly fused chorion and allantois, on the inner surface of the shell, are richly supplied with blood vessels, enabling the embryo to breathe through pores in the shell. The amnion is a further fluid-filled sac around the embryo that keeps it from drying out. The yolk-sac contains the embryonic food supply, rich in protein and fats. Eggs of this type are self-sufficient apart from respiration and some absorption of water from the environment.

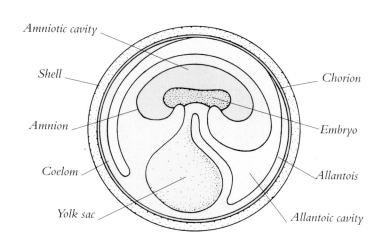

Amniotic cavity

Shell

Amnion

Coelom

Yolk sac

Chorion

Embryo

Allantois

Allantoic cavity

TURTLES AND TORTOISES

The 14 families of turtles and tortoises (chelonians) share an impressively armored shell, the upper part (carapace) of which is formed of bones that are fused with each other and with the animal's ribs and vertebrae. The lower section of the shell is called the plastron. Chelonians lack teeth, have internal fertilization, and lay shelled eggs. Some live in oceans, while others have adapted for life in a wide variety of terrestrial and aquatic habitats.

Central American River Turtle
Dermatemys mawii
This freshwater species inhabits rivers and lakes from southern Mexico to Honduras.

Green Sea Turtle
Chelonia mydas
Living in all tropical and temperate oceans, this species weighs up to 700 pounds (317 kg).

Yellow Mud Turtle
Kinosternon flavescens
An omnivorous freshwater species of central and southern United States and Mexico.

Seven ridges run along length of the carapace

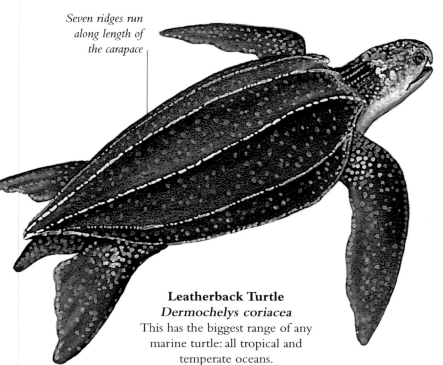

Leatherback Turtle
Dermochelys coriacea
This has the biggest range of any marine turtle: all tropical and temperate oceans.

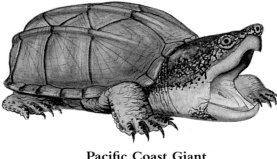

Pacific Coast Giant Musk Turtle
Staurotypus salvinii
Like other musk turtles, this Central American species is a carnivore.

Galápagos Giant Tortoise
Geochelone nigra
The Galápagos Islands, Ecuador, are home for this long-lived chelonian; one captive individual lived to the age of 170.

Eastern Box Turtle
Terrapene carolina
A declining species in the eastern United States and Mexico.

Leopard Tortoise
Geochelone pardalis
In very hot, or unusually cold, weather Leopard Tortoises take shelter in abandoned mammal burrows.

Alabama Red-bellied Turtle
Pseudemys alabamensis
This is the official reptile of the state of Alabama.

Paddlelike front flippers

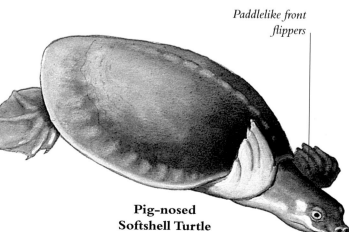

Pig-nosed Softshell Turtle
Carettochelys insculpta
This turtle is hunted for its meat in New Guinea; it also lives in parts of northern Australia.

Common Snapping Turtle
Chelydra serpentina
This aquatic ambush predator of eastern North America and Central America captures prey with its beaklike jaws.

LIZARDS

The lizards (order Squamata) are the most varied group of reptiles, with more than 5,000 species. Lizards exhibit more anatomical, behavioral, and reproductive diversity than any other reptiles. They are also spread farther and wider than other lizard groups, living on every continent except Antarctica. Most are active by day but others are nocturnal.

Arabian Toad-headed Lizard
Phrynocephalus arabicus
During the hottest parts of the day this desert-dweller stands high on extended legs to limit contact with the sand.

Fringe-toed Lizard
Uma notata
Fringes on the sides of this lizard's hind toes help it walk over soft sand in the deserts of North America.

Elongated scales form fringes on hind toes

Miscellaneous lizards
1. Common Asiatic Monitor, *Varanus salvator*, Southeast Asia. **2. Sungazer**, *Cordylus giganteus*, South Africa. **3. Chinese Xenosaur**, *Shinisaurus crocodilurus*, China, Vietnam. **4. Southern Alligator Lizard**, *Elgaria multicarinata*, Mexico, United States. **5. Bornean Earless Lizard**, *Lanthanotus borneensis*, Borneo. **6. Gila Monster**, *Heloderma suspectum*, Mexico, United States. **7. Asian Blind Lizard**, *Dibamus novaeguineae*, Indonesia, Papua New Guinea, Philippines.

1.

2.

3.

7.

Mediterranean Chameleon
Chamaeleo chamaeleon
It has the ability to change
color for camouflage, to signal
to other chameleons, and to
regulate its temperature.

Spiny-tailed Lizard
Uromastyx acanthinurus
This is a desert species that
can warn off enemies with
its spined tail.

4.

5.

6.

GECKOS AND SKINKS

The three families of geckos are mostly relatively small, insectivorous, nocturnal lizards. Many species are noted for their ability to climb and for their varied vocalizations. Most skinks (Scincidae) are active during the day, though some burrow-dwelling examples are nocturnal. They have roughly cylindrical bodies with short limbs.

Miscellaneous geckos and skinks
1. Madagascan Day Gecko, *Phelsuma liticauda, goeldii*, Madagascar. **2. Henshaw's Night Lizard**, *Xantusia henshawi*, United States, Mexico.
3. Moorish Gecko, *Tarentola mauritanica*, Mediterranean Basin. **4. Turkish Gecko**, *Hemidactylus turcicus*, Mediterranean Basin.
5. Common Tegu, *Tupinambis teguixin*, South America. **6. Ocellated Green Lizard**, *Lacerta lepida*, Spain. **7. Fat-tailed Gecko**, *Hemitheconyx caudocinctus*, West Africa. **8. Western Skink**, *Eumeces skiltonianus*, western United States.
9. Western Blue-tongued Skink, *Tiliqua occipitalis*, Australia. **10. Common Checkered Whiptail**, *Cnemidiphorus tesselatus*, United States, Mexico.

1.

2.

3.

4.

5.

6.

7.

8.

9.

10.

SNAKES

SNAKES

There are more than 3,200 species in 18–20 families. They are legless reptiles and have evolved specialized methods of locomotion and sensing the world around them. Some use venom to immobilize their prey, while others constrict animals that are sometimes larger than themselves; most simply swallow their prey. Smell is their most important sense.

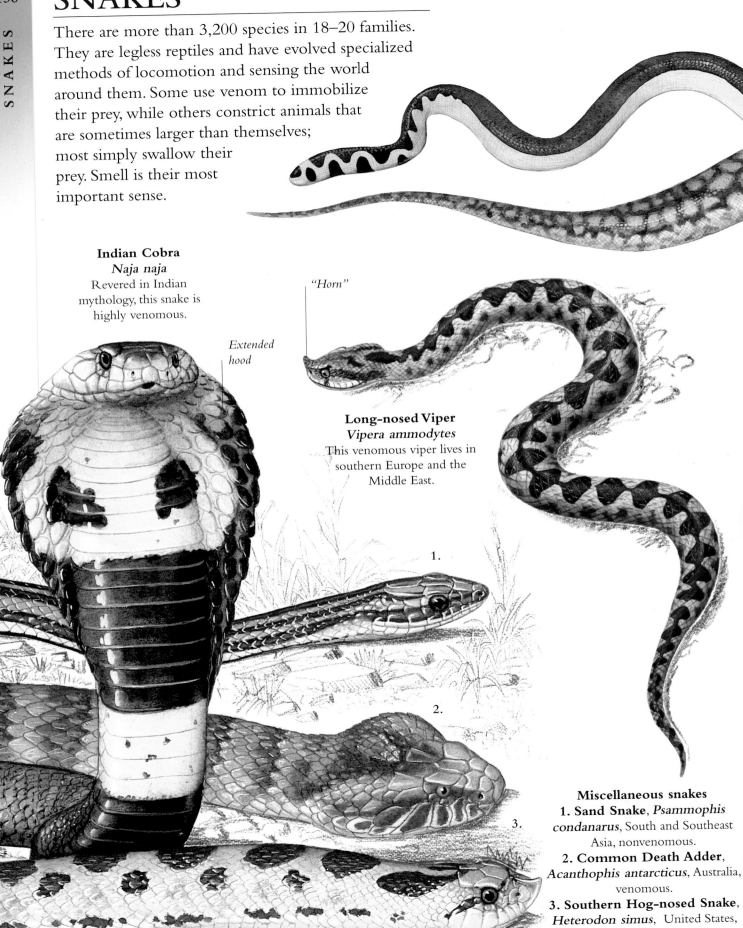

Indian Cobra
Naja naja
Revered in Indian mythology, this snake is highly venomous.

"Horn"

Extended hood

Long-nosed Viper
Vipera ammodytes
This venomous viper lives in southern Europe and the Middle East.

1.

2.

3.

Miscellaneous snakes
1. **Sand Snake,** *Psammophis condanarus,* South and Southeast Asia, nonvenomous.
2. **Common Death Adder,** *Acanthophis antarcticus,* Australia, venomous.
3. **Southern Hog-nosed Snake,** *Heterodon simus,* United States, nonvenomous.

Yellow-bellied Seasnake
Pelamis platurus
Adapted for life in tropical Indian
and Pacific waters, this venomous snake
is helpless on land.

"Baggy" skin

Arafura Filesnake
Acrochordus arafurae
Coastal New Guinea and
northern Australia.
Nonvenomous

Red-bellied Water Snake
Nerodia erythrogaster
United States and Mexico.
Nonvenomous

Eastern Racer
Coluber constrictor
North and Central America.
Nonvenomous

Sidewinder
Crotalus cerastes
A species of the south-
western United States,
this venomous species
lives in deserts.

"Rattle"

Mamushi
Gloydius blomhoffii
China, Japan, and Korea.
Venomous

**Yellow-bellied
House Snake**
Lamprophis fuscus
South Africa.
Nonvenomous

CROCODILIANS

Crocodilians are highly predatory reptiles. Most inhabit aquatic environments—from small pools to coastal oceanic waters—in the tropics. Some hunt exclusively in the water, while others may also take prey on land. Crocodiles (family Crocodylidae) and alligators (Alligatoridae) have different tooth patterns but have essentially similar lifestyles. The only other crocodilian is the critically endangered Gharial (Gavialidae) of South Asia, whose diet is almost exclusively fish.

Short snout

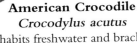

American Crocodile
Crocodylus acutus
Inhabits freshwater and brackish environments in coastal United States, where it hunts and eats fish, frogs, turtles, and occasionally small mammals and birds. Can reach 20 feet (6.1 m) in length.

Chinese Alligator
Alligator sinensis
A relatively small alligator, this species of the Yangtze River basin in China is now critically endangered.

Cuvier's Dwarf Caiman, *Paleosuchus palpebrosus* (top), and **Dwarf Crocodile,** *Osteolaemus tetraspis,* are small crocodilians of South America and West Africa, respectively. Both grow to a maximum length of about 54 inches (1.4 m).

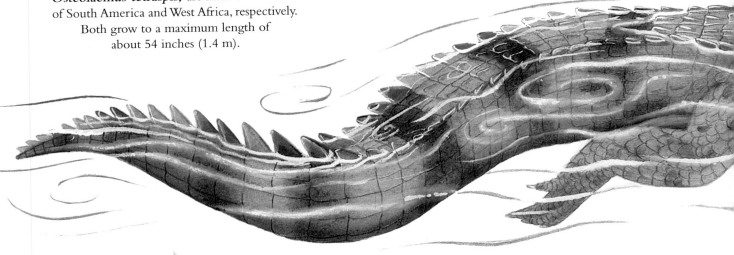

Black Caiman
Melanosuchus niger
This is the largest predator in the Amazon Basin, growing to 20 feet (6.1 m) and eating piranhas, catfish, and capybaras.

American Alligator
Alligator mississippiensis
Lives in freshwater swamps and lakes in the United States. Males grow to 16 feet 8 inches (4.5 m).

Mugger
Crocodylus palustris
A top predator in South Asian lakes and rivers, the Mugger has the broadest snout of any crocodile.

Gharial
Gavialis gangeticus
Adaptations for a fish-eating diet include a long, thin snout and 110 small teeth. This crocodilian grows to 20 feet (6.1 m). The Gharial is critically endangered.

Slender-snouted Crocodile
Crocodylus cataphractus
It hunts mammals that visit the margins of Central African rivers and lakes to drink.

False Gharial
Tomistoma schlegelii
Its snout is similar to that of a Gharial, but this Southeast Asian species has a more general diet than its fish-eating cousin. This individual is carrying two of its young.

WHAT IS A FISH?

Fishes are aquatic, ectothermic (cold-blooded), gill-breathing vertebrates. They demonstrate great diversity. There are five separate classes: jawless lampreys, hagfish, cartilaginous fishes, lobe-finned fishes, and bony fishes. There are more bony fishes than all the other species combined. Some fishes live exclusively in fresh water or saltwater, while others are able to live in either environment.

▼ FISH FINS

Fins give a fish control over its movement by directing forward thrust and providing lift. There are usually two sets of paired fins—the pectorals and the pelvics—and two single ones—the dorsal and anal, in addition to the caudal (tail) complex.

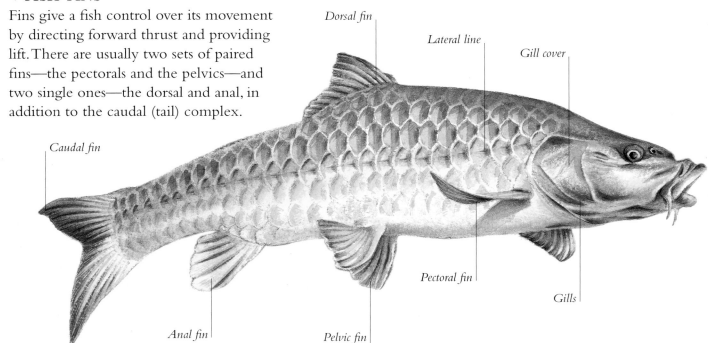

Dorsal fin

Lateral line

Gill cover

Caudal fin

Pectoral fin

Gills

Anal fin

Pelvic fin

▶ GILL STRUCTURES

1. Hagfishes: water passes through a series of muscular pouches before it leaves through a single opening.

2. Lampreys: each gill has a separate opening to the outside, and the gills are supported by a branchial basket.

3. Sharks: the gills open directly to the outside via five gill slits.

4. Bony fishes: the gills are protected externally by a bony cover called an operculum.

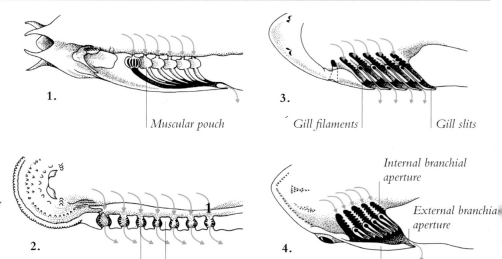

1.

Muscular pouch

3.

Gill filaments

Gill slits

2.

Gill filaments

Branchial basket

4.

Internal branchial aperture

External branchial aperture

Operculum

▼ BONY FISH SKELETON

Bony fishes have a skeleton formed of true bone. Typically, there are vertebrae and two pairs of ribs. The fin rays are composed of bony, segmented rays, which may be modified into hard spines.

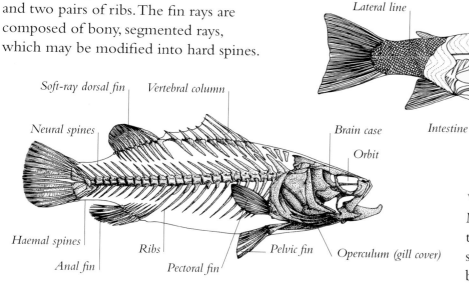

Soft-ray dorsal fin | Vertebral column

Neural spines

Brain case

Orbit

Haemal spines

Ribs

Anal fin

Pectoral fin

Pelvic fin

Operculum (gill cover)

Lateral line · Kidney · Swimbladder · Pneumatic duct · Brain · Gill arches · Olfactory bulb

Intestine · Spleen · Liver · Stomach · Heart · Jaw muscles

▼ BONY FISH ORGANS

Many of a fish's organs are similar to those of other vertebrates. The swimbladder, which provides buoyancy, is unique to fish.

▶ SHARK SKELETON

Sharks, skates, rays, and chimaeras have a cartilaginous skeleton. Vertebrae are formed by layers of cartilage around the notochord. There are fins but their rays are soft and unsegmented.

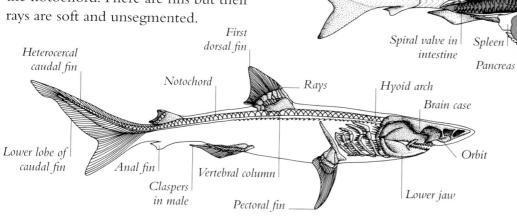

Myotomes (muscle blocks) · Ovary · Kidney · Liver · Brain · Eye · Gill slits

Spiral valve in intestine · Spleen · Pancreas · Heart · Jaw muscles · Olfactory organ

Heterocercal caudal fin

First dorsal fin

Notochord · Rays · Hyoid arch

Brain case

Lower lobe of caudal fin

Anal fin

Claspers in male

Vertebral column

Pectoral fin

Orbit

Lower jaw

▼ SHARK ORGANS

Buoyancy is provided by a large, oily liver instead of a swimbladder.

MOUTH SHAPES

1. Moorish Idol, *Zanclus cornutus,* has a protruding mouth with bristlelike teeth for scraping tiny creatures off rocks.

2. Angel Squeaker, *Synodontis angelicus,* has long mouth barbels; these help it locate food.

3. Siamese Fighting Fish, *Betta splendens,* has an upturned mouth, ideal for catching insect larvae.

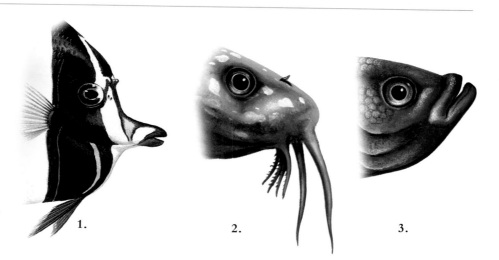

1.   2.   3.

EELS AND LAMPREYS

There are more than 800 species of eels in 28 families. Anatomically, they are very diverse but they are united by their reproductive biology: they all have a larval (leptocephalus) stage, and the newly hatched young look very different from the adults. Lampreys and hagfish (superclass Agnatha) have neither jaws nor backbones. They are not closely related to each other but are both described as "primitive fish."

Gulper Eel
Eurypharynx pelecanoides
This eel lives at depths down to 9,800 feet (3,000 m). It has a bioluminescent light at the tip of its tail.

European Conger Eel
Conger conger
This large, aggressive predator often lives in wrecks and rocky areas on the seafloor.

Notacanth
Halosaurus species
This species grows to 6 feet (1.8 m) in length and lives at great depths.

Snipe eels
The longer fish is one of the *Nemichthys snipe eels;* it grows to 43 inches (1.1 m). The other eel is the much smaller **Curtailed Snipe Eel,** *Cyema atrum,* which has a maximum length of 6 inches (15 cm).

Seagrass Eel
Chilorhinus suensonii
A resident of sandy seafloor and seagrass beds, this eel hunts small fish and invertebrates.

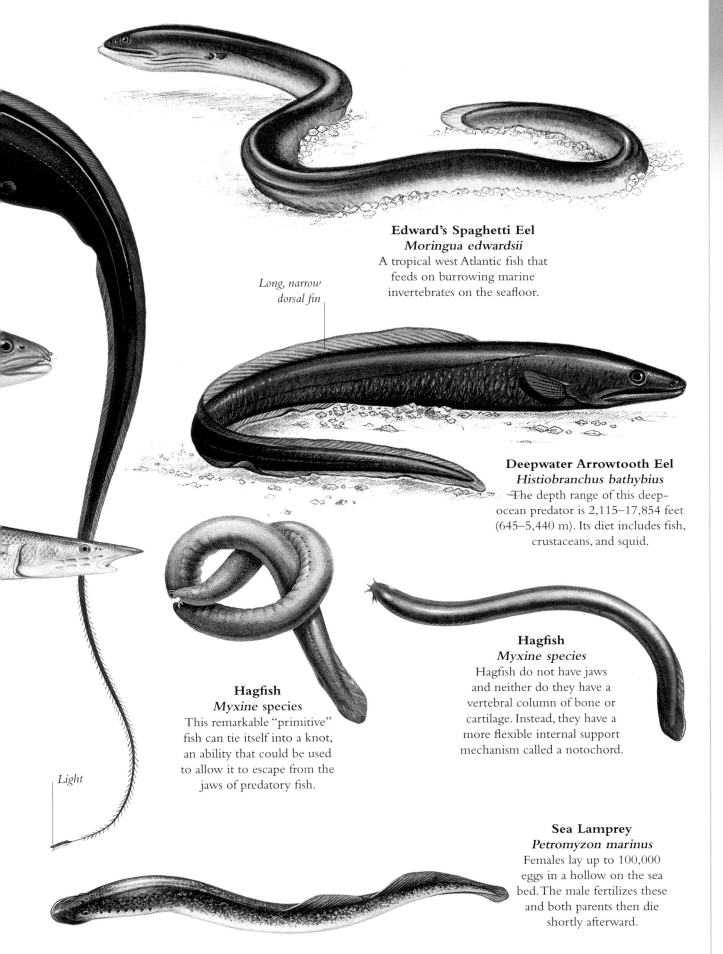

Edward's Spaghetti Eel
Moringua edwardsii
A tropical west Atlantic fish that
feeds on burrowing marine
invertebrates on the seafloor.

*Long, narrow
dorsal fin*

Deepwater Arrowtooth Eel
Histiobranchus bathybius
The depth range of this deep-
ocean predator is 2,115–17,854 feet
(645–5,440 m). Its diet includes fish,
crustaceans, and squid.

Hagfish
Myxine species
Hagfish do not have jaws
and neither do they have a
vertebral column of bone or
cartilage. Instead, they have a
more flexible internal support
mechanism called a notochord.

Hagfish
Myxine species
This remarkable "primitive"
fish can tie itself into a knot,
an ability that could be used
to allow it to escape from the
jaws of predatory fish.

Light

Sea Lamprey
Petromyzon marinus
Females lay up to 100,000
eggs in a hollow on the sea
bed. The male fertilizes these
and both parents then die
shortly afterward.

HERRINGS, STURGEONS, AND BONEYTONGUES

The herrings (order Clupeiformes) are 360 or so species of oceanic fish, all with a relatively similar body form. Sturgeons (order Acipenseriformes) include some of the largest freshwater fish, the bottom-dwelling goliaths. Bonytongues (Osteoglossiformes) uniquely have tongues bearing well-developed teeth.

Arapaima
Arapaima gigas
This large bonytongue builds a nest for its young in the sandy bed of a river in the Amazon Basin.

Giant Featherback
Chitala lopis
Growing to 5 feet (1.5 m), this Southeast Asian bonytongue varies from bronze to silver in color.

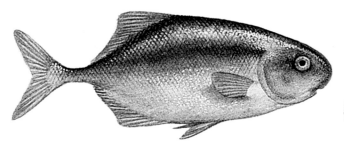

Northern Churchill
Petrocephalus catastoma
A resident of the Rovuma River system of East Africa, this fish usually favors muddy waters.

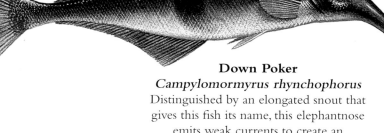

Down Poker
Campylomormyrus rhynchophorus
Distinguished by an elongated snout that gives this fish its name, this elephantnose emits weak currents to create an "electric image" of its surroundings in muddy African rivers.

"Paddle" is one third of fish's length

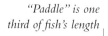

American Paddlefish
Polyodon spathula
Some people believe that sensory cells in the unique paddle help this fish detect food in North American rivers.

African Butterfly Fish
Pantodon buchholzi
Swimming in West African forest pools and swamps, this fish always remains close to the water surface. It takes surface-living invertebrates and fish, and—by leaping out of the water—flying insects also.

Silver Arowana
Osteoglossum bicirrhosum
Arowanas can jump almost 3 feet (0.9 m) out of the water to seize flying insects, birds, and even bats in their native Amazon and Orinoco basins.

Dorab Wolf Herring
Chirocentrus dorab
A long, slender, voracious predator found in the Indo-Pacific from the Red Sea and East Africa to northern Australia.

Rows of bony scutes run along body

Baltic Sturgeon
Acipenser sturio
This large fish migrates from the ocean to freshwater spawning grounds, where it lays its eggs in water flowing over gravel.

Pallid Sturgeon
Scaphirhynchus albus
This North American species lives in the Missouri River and the lower Mississippi River.

PIKE AND SALMON

Fish of the superorder Protacanthopterygii are found in oceans worldwide and in fresh water in North America and northern Eurasia. Pike (family Esocidae) are mainly freshwater fish; salmon, trout, and their allies (Salmonidae) are extremely important commercial fish in the Northern Hemisphere. Some species are anadromous: they spawn in fresh water but spend most of their life at sea.

Grayling
Thymallus thymallus
A resident of freshwater rivers and lakes in northern Europe, this species favors cold, clean water.

Argentine
Argentina sphyraena
This species probably schools near the seafloor on the east Atlantic continental shelf.

Ayu
Plecoglossus altivelis
A fish of rivers, lakes, and coastal waters in and around Japan, Korea, and China.

Mirrorbelly
Opisthoproctus grimaldii
The Mirrorbelly is found in tropical and subtropical Atlantic and Pacific Ocean waters between 984–1,312 feet (300–400 m) deep.

Aulostomatomorpha
Aulostomatomorpha species
Lives on continental slopes at depths of 5,580–6,560 feet (1,700–2,000 m) in tropical Indian and Pacific waters

Pencil smelt species
Xenophthalmichthys danae
This eel-like fish lives in tropical waters of the Atlantic and Pacific oceans to depths of 4,100 feet (1,250 m).

Sockeye Salmon
Oncorhynchus nerka
This anadromous species
spawns in freshwater lakes and
rivers in North America.

Rainbow Trout
Oncorhynchus mykiss
A native of the Pacific coast of
North America, this trout has
been introduced to every
other continent except
Antarctica.

Sea Trout
Salmo trutta trutta
An oceanic species that returns
to fresh water only to spawn
in swift-flowing rivers.

Arctic Charr
Salvelinus alpinus
Some charr spend their whole
life in fresh water, while others
are anadromous.

Shortjaw cisco (left)
Coregonus zenithicus
A fish of deep water in the
Great Lakes of the United
States and Canada.

Atlantic Salmon
Salmo salar
This very important commercial
fish lives in the North Atlantic
except when it returns to
rivers to spawn.

BRISTLEMOUTHS AND ANGLERFISH

The deep-ocean bristlemouths (order Stomiiformes) feature bristlelike teeth and luminous organs. They are flesh-eating fish with large, gaping mouths. Most anglerfish (Lophiiformes) have the first dorsal-fin spine on the tip of the snout, and this is modified as a fishing apparatus. Some anglerfish live as deep as 12,140 feet (3,700 m).

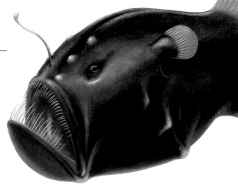

Humpback Anglerfish
Melanocetus johnsonii
This is a female, which grows to 7 inches (18 cm), dwarfing the 1-inch (2.5 cm) male.

American Oyster Toadfish
Opsanus tau
A venomous species in the family Batrachoididae, which hunts in the shallow waters of the western Atlantic and Caribbean.

Frogfish
Antennariidae species
Frogfish are species of anglerfish that live in most tropical and subtropical oceans, where they lie in wait for prey on the seafloor.

Anglerfish
Linophryne species
A small anglerfish, no more than 3 inches (7 cm) long, with an elaborate lure and a large branched barbel hanging from the chin.

Whipnose Anglerfish
Gigantactis species
The fish is 6 inches (15 cm) long but has a thin illicium, or "fishing rod," which is several times longer.

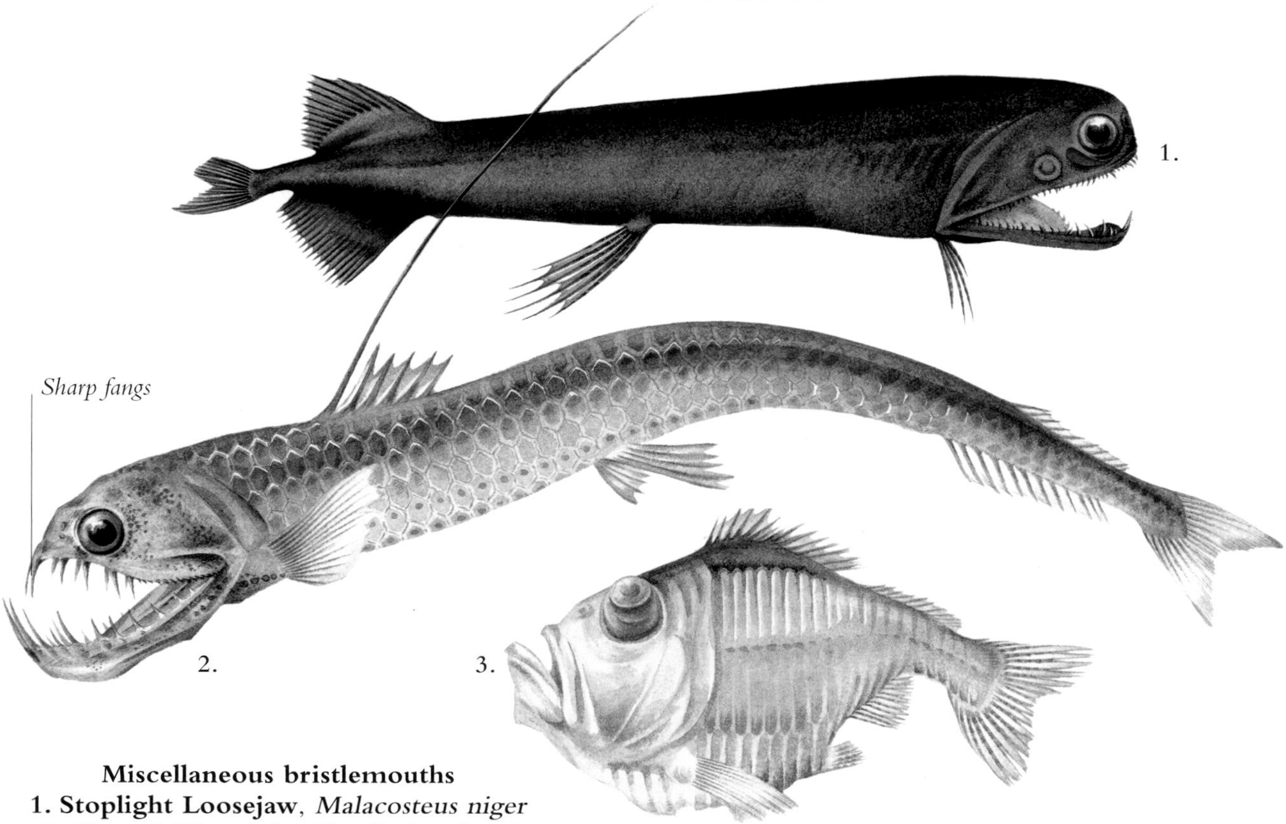

Sharp fangs

Miscellaneous bristlemouths
1. Stoplight Loosejaw, *Malacosteus niger*
2. Sloane's Viperfish, *Chauliodus sloani*
3. Pacific Hatchetfish, *Argyropelecus affinis*

Barbel

American Goosefish
Lophius americanus
This 4-foot (1.2 m) member
of the family Lophiidae is a
voracious predator in the
western Atlantic.

Barbeled Dragonfish
*Grammatostomias
flagellibarba*
A deep-ocean species with a
loop of bioluminescent tissues
on the flanks and a luminous
cell at the tip of its long barbel.

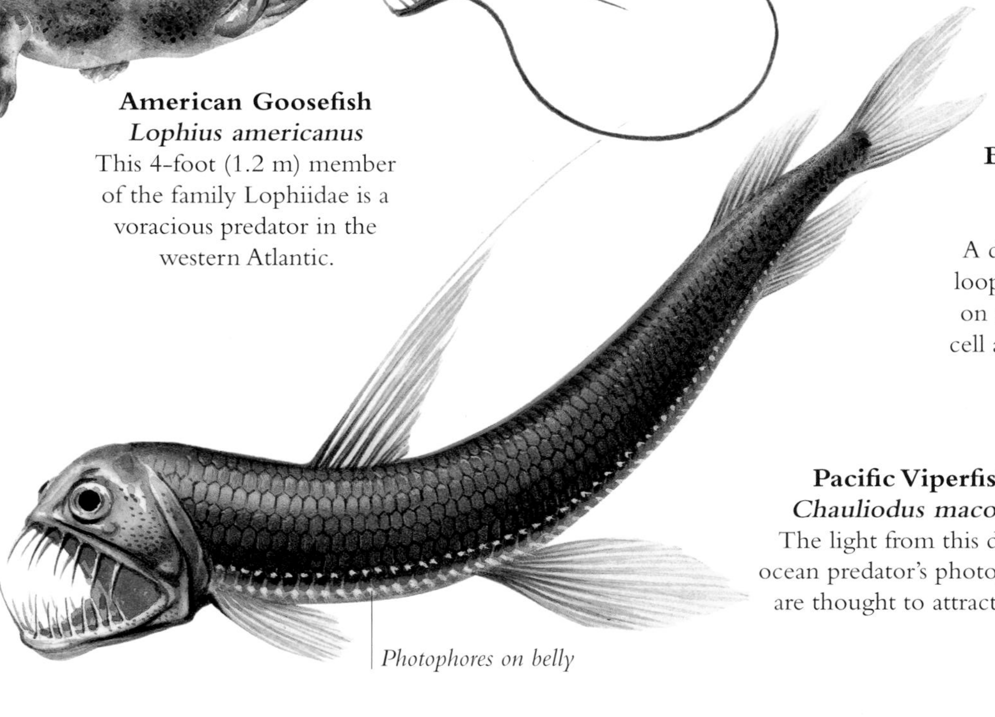

Pacific Viperfish
Chauliodus macouni
The light from this deep-
ocean predator's photophores
are thought to attract prey.

Photophores on belly

CARP AND CATFISH

There are about 2,700 species of carp in five families (order Cypriniformes). Native to North America, Africa, and Eurasia, they are mostly freshwater, egg-laying species and include the world's largest riverine fish. Most of the 2,400 or so varieties of catfish (order Siluriformes) are tropical freshwater species, but some inhabit temperate regions and two families are marine.

Hardhead Catfish
Arius felis
The male mouth-broods the eggs until they hatch.

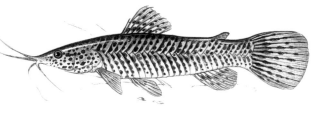

Slender Armored Catfish
Callichthys callichthys
This species (left) often forms shoals and is common in rivers and lakes in parts of South America.

Mahseer
Tor tor
Often found in fast-flowing rivers in Asia, the Mahseer can grow to 57 inches (1.5 m).

Common Carp
Cyprinus carpio
The female lays more than 1 million sticky eggs in the vegetation of shallow waters.

Long Spiky-head Carp
Luciobrama macrocephalus
A pikelike predator living in rivers and lakes in Southeast Asia.

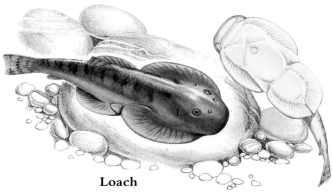

Loach
Gastromyzon species
The paired fins of this loach form suction disks, allowing it to cling to rocks in fast-flowing hill streams.

Gudgeon
Gobio gobio
A native of Europe, swimming in lakes, reservoirs, and both fast-flowing and slow-flowing rivers.

Red Shiner
Cyprinella lutrensis
A colorful species that lives in the
United States and Mexico.

Ghost Knifefish, *Apteronotus albifrons,*
and **Electric Knifefish,** *Electrophorus
electricus*

Milkfish
Chanos chanos
This streamlined tropical
oceanic species (below) has
a large caudal fin.

Rosy Barb
Barbus conchonius
These tiny carp live in freshwater
rivers. The brighter fish on the
right is the male.

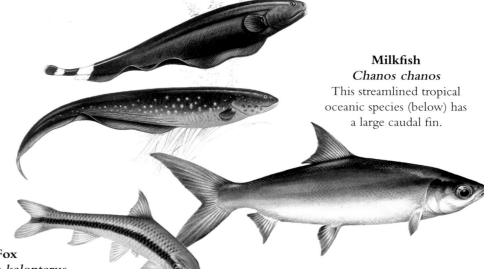

Flying Fox
Epalzeorhynchos kalopterus
A native of South and Southeast
Asia and Africa.

Walking Catfish
Clarias batrachus
This uses its pectoral fins to
wriggle across muddy surfaces.

Channel Catfish
Ictalurus punctatus
This is a popular sport
fish in North America.

Upside-down Catfish
Synodontis nigriventris
This fish swims upside-down
to graze the underside of
leaves for algae.

Wels Catfish
Silurus glanis
Adults of this, the second-largest catfish
in the world, often reach around
10 feet (3 m) in length and weigh more
than 440 pounds (200 kg).

Giant Catfish
Pangasianodon gigas
The world's largest freshwater fish lives in
the Mekong River, China, and Tonle Sap,
Cambodia, but it is critically endangered.

Indian Frogmouth Catfish
Chaca chaca
This fish has been described as
looking like a flattened leaf with a
huge mouth at one end.

CODFISH AND SILVERSIDES

There are almost 500 species of codfish (order Gadiformes). They are found in all the world's oceans and one is confined to fresh water. Most cuskeel species (order Ophidiiformes) are marine, some living at great depths. In contrast, all the trout-perches (order Percopsiformes) live in freshwater rivers and lakes in North America.

Luminous Hake
Steindachneria argentea
Luminous Hake (right) are often common in deep water (1,300–1,640 feet, 400–500 m) in the Gulf of Mexico.

Thread-tailed Grenadier
Coryphaenoides filicauda
This long-tailed deepwater species (right) of the Southern Ocean lives at depths to 16,400 feet (5,000 m).

Very long tail

Large dorsal fin

Atlantic Cod
Gadus morhua
Overfishing has meant that populations of this commercially fished species have declined dramatically.

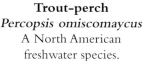

Pirate Perch
Aphredoderus sayanus
Feeding at night, this freshwater species is common in parts of North America.

Trout-perch
Percopsis omiscomaycus
A North American freshwater species.

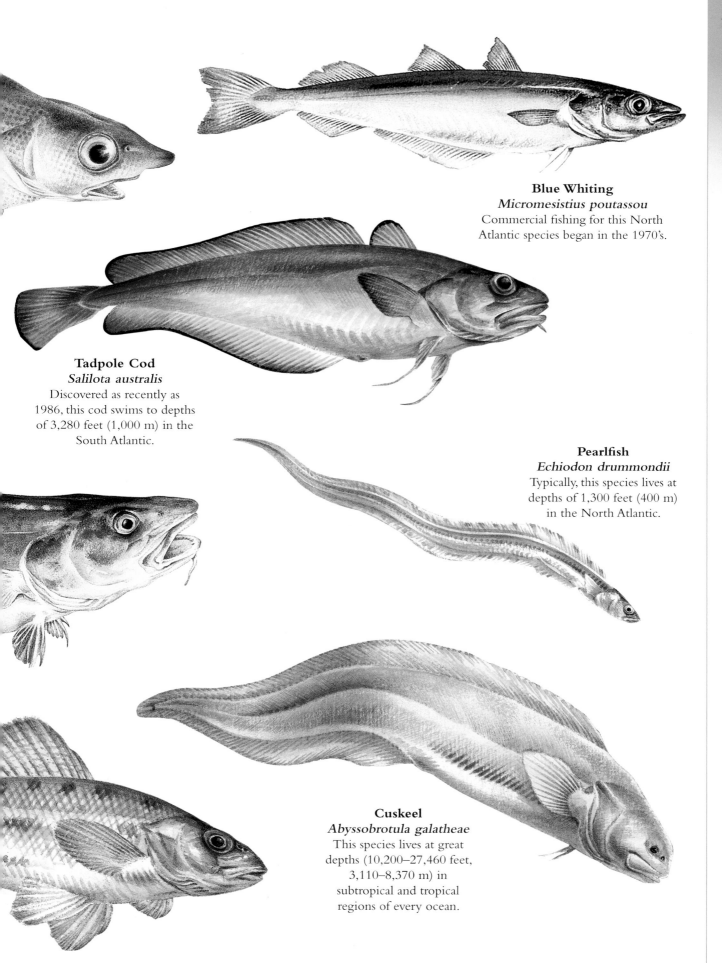

Blue Whiting
Micromesistius poutassou
Commercial fishing for this North
Atlantic species began in the 1970's.

Tadpole Cod
Salilota australis
Discovered as recently as
1986, this cod swims to depths
of 3,280 feet (1,000 m) in the
South Atlantic.

Pearlfish
Echiodon drummondii
Typically, this species lives at
depths of 1,300 feet (400 m)
in the North Atlantic.

Cuskeel
Abyssobrotula galatheae
This species lives at great
depths (10,200–27,460 feet,
3,110–8,370 m) in
subtropical and tropical
regions of every ocean.

PERCHLIKE FISH

No other order of fishes comes close to the
Perciformes in terms of the number of species (more
than 9,300, which is 40 per cent of all fish), nor the
variety of structure and ecology. Perch live worldwide
in marine and freshwater environments, and range
from small, delicate angelfish to large, fast-swimming
predators such as barracudas and swordfish.

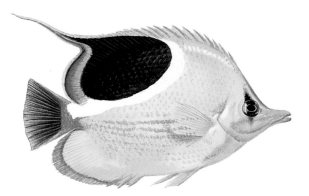

Saddleback Butterflyfish
Chaetodon ephippium
Lives around coral reefs in tropical
Indian and Pacific Oceans.

Totoaba
Totoaba macdonaldi
This species faces extinction
due to overfishing for its
swimbladder, which is
considered a delicacy by
some people.

Atlantic Blue Marlin
Makaira nigricans
This formidable, fast-swimming predator
feeds on fish, squid, and octopuses.

Dwarf Pygmy Goby
Pandaka pygmaea
A critically endangered mangrove species
of Indonesia, this goby is probably now
extinct in the Philippines.

Achilles Tang
Acanthurus achilles
Lives around coral reefs in
the Pacific Ocean, where it
feeds on algae.

Yellow Labidochromis
Labidochromis caeruleus
A mouth-brooding cichlid that
lives only in freshwater Lake
Malawi, East Africa.

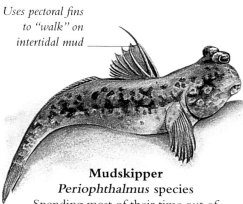

*Uses pectoral fins
to "walk" on
intertidal mud*

Mudskipper
Periophthalmus species
Spending most of their time out of
water, mudskippers are inhabitants
of mangroves around the coasts of
Africa and southern Asia.

Atlantic Mackerel
Scomber scombrus
This important
fisheries species lives
in cold and temperate
regions of the North
Atlantic.

Yellow-fin Tuna
Thunnus albacares
Growing to 400 pounds (180 kg), this
is a fast-swimming, commercial food
fish of tropical and subtropical waters.

Sickle-shaped anal fin

Regal Angelfish
Pygoplites diacanthus
Coral reefs in the Indo-Pacific
are this colorful species' (left)
favored habitat.

Princess Parrotfish
Scarus taeniopterus
A colorful resident of tropical
reefs in the Caribbean Sea
and the western Atlantic.

LANTERNFISH, LUNGFISH, AND LIZARDFISH

Lanternfish (order Myctophiformes) are deep-sea marine fish. Lungfish (three families) can breathe air and live out of water for days to months, depending on the species. Lizardfish (Aulopiformes) are a diverse group with a peculiar arrangement of the small bones in the gills. Coelacanths (Coelacanthidae) are still poorly known.

Metallic Lanternfish
Myctophum affine
This fish grows to just 3 inches (8 cm) and feeds on plankton in the Atlantic Ocean.

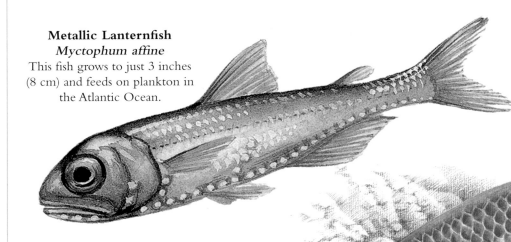

Long-snouted Lancetfish
Alepisaurus ferox
This highly predatory fish lives in tropical, subtropical, and temperate oceans, sometimes at great depths.

Queensland Lungfish
Neoceratodus forsteri
One of only six living species of air-breathing lungfishes, it can survive for several days out of water as long as its skin is moist.

BICHIRS, COELACANTHS, AND LUNGFISHES

The five different families demonstrate a great variety of body forms. Note the absence of dorsal fins on the lungfishes, in comparison with the two pronounced fins of the coelacanths and the row of small finlets along a bichir's back, each of which consists of a stout spine supporting a series of rays.

NB: the diagrams are not to scale and show only typical species.

1. **Bichirs**, *family Polypteridae*
2. **Coelacanths**, *Coelacanthidae*
3. **Australian lungfishes**, *Ceradontidae*
4. **South American lungfishes**, *Lepidosirenidae*
5. **African lungfishes**, *Protopteridae*

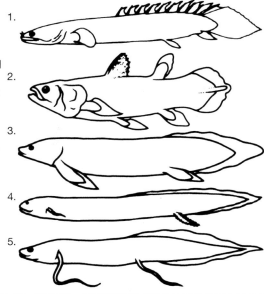

Short-finned Bichir
Polypterus palmas
Adults of this swamp-dwelling fish can breathe air; they live in coastal rivers of the Guinea Gulf, from Guinea Bissau to Liberia.

Spotted Moonfish
Lampris guttatus
Sometimes taken as by-catch in longline fishing for tuna, this lives in tropical and temperate oceans worldwide.

Prominent crest

Indo–Pacific Graceful Lizardfish
Saurida gracilis
This fish is common in shallow lagoons and reef flats in the Indian and Pacific oceans.

Giant Oarfish
Regalecus glesne
This, the world's longest bony fish, may grow to 36 feet (11 m) or more. Its fin rays form a distinctive red crest.

West Indian Ocean Coelacanth
Latimeria chalumnae
Previously known only from fossils, the first living example of this fish was found as recently as 1938.

SKATES, RAYS, AND SHARKS

The gill slits of skates and rays (order Rajiformes) are on the underside of the body. These fish have a cartilaginous skeleton, as do sharks (class Chondrichthyes). The latter have well-developed senses and give birth to live young. Some sharks are fearsome predators.

Great White Shark
Carcharodon carcharias
Found in all the main oceans, this apex predator grows to 21 feet (6.4 m) and has no natural predators apart from the Killer Whale.

Marbled Electric Ray
Torpedo sinuspersici
Associated with reefs in the Indian Ocean, this ray can deliver a nasty shock.

Cephalic fin either side of mouth

Whale Shark
Rhincodon typus
This is the largest living fish species, growing to 47,000 pounds (21.5 tonnes) and 41 feet (12.6 m). It is a slow-swimming filter-feeder found in tropical and subtropical oceans around the world.

Long tail

Manta Ray
Manta birostris
Living mostly in tropical and subtropical ocean waters, this ray's fins can attain a span of up to 23 feet (7 m).

Common Guitarfish
Rhinobatos rhinobatos
A bottom-dwelling inhabitant of shallow waters in the eastern Atlantic from France to Angola, and in the Mediterranean Sea.

Rabbitfish
Chimaera monstrosa
This fish has venomous spines.
It mostly feeds on bottom-
living invertebrates.

Venomous spine

Ornate Angelshark
Squatina tergocellata
This angelshark lives off the coasts of
western and southern Australia, above
the continental shelf and the upper
continental slope.

Cuban Ribbontail Catshark
Eridacnis barbouri
Lives at depths of 1,300–2,130
feet (400–650 m) around the
coasts of northern South
America, the Gulf of Mexico,
and the Caribbean Sea.

Large pectoral fin

Leopard Shark
Triakis semifasciata
This beautifully marked shark
lives mostly in inshore waters
on the Pacific coast of
North America.

Ocellate River Stingray
Potamotrygon motoro
This is a freshwater fish that
lives in South America. Its tail
can deliver a powerful sting.

WHAT IS AN INSECT?

The insects (class Insecta) are small invertebrates with six legs and generally one or two pairs of wings. The body of a typical adult insect is divided into the head, thorax (bearing the legs and wings), and abdomen. The class includes many familiar forms, such as flies, bees, wasps, moths, beetles, grasshoppers, and cockroaches. More than one million species of insects have been described.

▼ INSECT ANATOMY

Cuticle, which forms the exoskeleton, is central to insects' success. Most insect sense organs are modifications of the cuticle itself. The most common form occurs as bristles (setae), which may be articulated so the nerve ending within the bristle shaft is stimulated when the bristle moves.

Compound eye
Antenna
Brain
Heart
Foregut
Hemocoel
Crop
Midgut
Diverticula
Malpighian tubules
Segment
Hindgut
Salivary glands
Mouth
Rectum
Mouthparts
Trochanter
Nerve cord
Gonad
Spiracles
Air sac
Femur

CUTICLE

SENSORY SYSTEMS

NERVOUS SYSTEM

DIGESTION

EXCRETION

RESPIRATION

CIRCULATION

Extensor muscle

Flexor muscle

Movement when flexor contracts

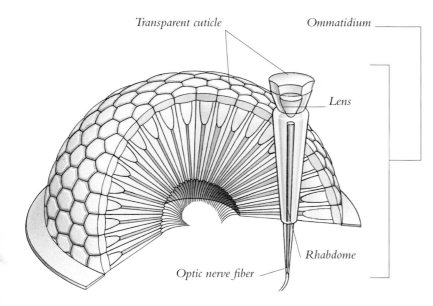

Transparent cuticle

Ommatidium

Lens

Rhabdome

Optic nerve fiber

◀ **COMPOUND EYES**

The compound eyes of insects and other arthropods consist of up to 30,000 individual lenses in pigment-containing visual units called ommatidia. Each ommatidium has a narrow field of vision, but the images from adjacent ommatidia overlap. Each one has two focusing lenses: a cornea of transparant cuticle and a crystalline lens.

▶ **BODY SEGMENTS**

Each body segment is essentially a box, with the tergum forming the roof, the sternum the floor, and the pleura the sides. Legs emerge from the lower sides of the pleura and are operated by retractor and protractor muscles connected to the main plates of the body to raise or lower the legs.

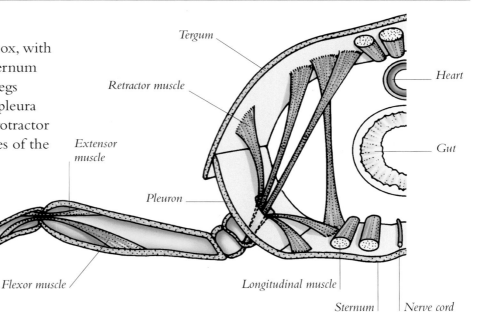

Tergum

Retractor muscle

Extensor muscle

Heart

Gut

Pleuron

Flexor muscle

Longitudinal muscle

Sternum

Nerve cord

▼ ▶ **HOW INSECTS BREATHE**

Insects breathe through pores, or spiracles, in the cuticle. These connect to tracheal tubes and air sacs. The main features of a grasshopper's respiratory system are illustrated.

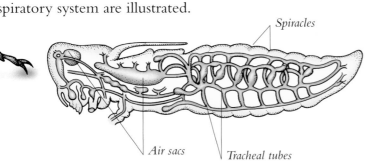

Spiracles

Air sacs

Tracheal tubes

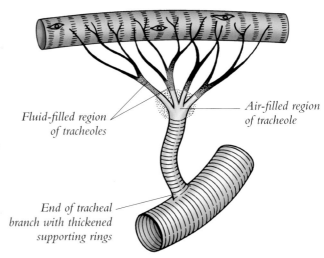

Fluid-filled region of tracheoles

Air-filled region of tracheole

End of tracheal branch with thickened supporting rings

ANTS AND WASPS

All ants (family Formicidae) are social insects. Queen ants lay eggs; soldiers focus on the defense of the colony; and workers are divided between foragers and those caring for the queen's brood. Ant societies have been looked upon as "super societies," in which component individuals may be lost without disabling the organism as a whole. Most wasp species (more than 100,000, in many families) are parasitic, using their ovipositor to lay eggs directly into a host species. Most true wasps are solitary hunters, though some are social.

Wingspan is 1 inch (2.5 cm) or more

1.

2.

Swollen abdomen

Varied ant behaviors

1. Workers of species in the genus ***Myrmecocystus*** do not leave the nest but are fed with nectar and honeydew, becoming "living storage jars" for the colony in times of drought.

2. Black Garden Ant, *Lasius niger*, workers tend aphids. In return for the ants' protection against predators, the aphids provide the ants with sweet honeydew.

3. Australian Bulldog Ant, *Myrmecia gulosa*, underground nest chamber with eggs, larvae, and pupae.

Pupal cocoon

3.

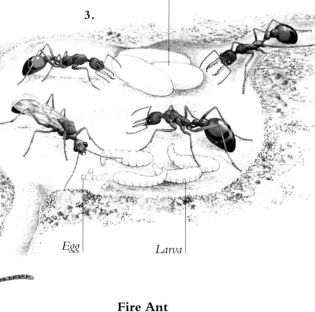

Egg   *Larva*

Fire Ant
Solenopsis geminata
This species is a serious crop pest. Its name derives from the burning sensation caused by its venomous bite.

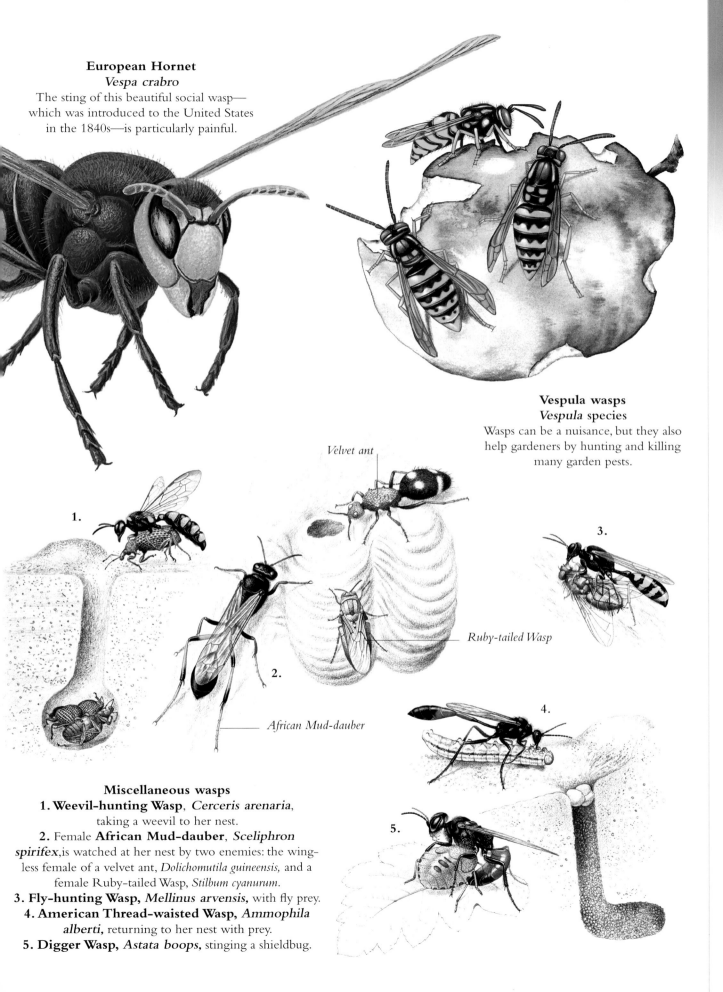

European Hornet
Vespa crabro
The sting of this beautiful social wasp— which was introduced to the United States in the 1840s—is particularly painful.

Vespula wasps
Vespula species
Wasps can be a nuisance, but they also help gardeners by hunting and killing many garden pests.

Velvet ant

1.

3.

2.

Ruby-tailed Wasp

African Mud-dauber

4.

5.

Miscellaneous wasps
1. Weevil-hunting Wasp, *Cerceris arenaria,* taking a weevil to her nest.
2. Female **African Mud-dauber**, *Sceliphron spirifex,* is watched at her nest by two enemies: the wing-less female of a velvet ant, *Dolichomutila guineensis,* and a female Ruby-tailed Wasp, *Stilbum cyanurum.*
3. Fly-hunting Wasp, *Mellinus arvensis,* with fly prey.
4. American Thread-waisted Wasp, *Ammophila alberti,* returning to her nest with prey.
5. Digger Wasp, *Astata boops,* stinging a shieldbug.

BUTTERFLIES

Butterflies and moths belong to the extremely diverse order Lepidoptera. Colorful members of this huge group are some of the most familiar of all insects. The name Lepidoptera means "scale-wing" and is derived from the thousands of tiny scales that cover the wings of most members of the group. The wings need to provide efficient flight, but they have other uses as well, notably in courtship displays to attract members of the opposite sex.

Red-banded Purple
Limenitis artemis
Also known as the "fall butterfly" because of its late flight period

Female lays eggs on selected leaves

Queen Alexandra's Birdwing
Ornithoptera alexandrae
This butterfly has a wingspan of 11 inches (28 cm).

Female _____

Venus Swift Moth
Leto venus
The larvae of this moth feed in tree trunks in its native South Africa.

Note the bright orange-red "eye-spots"

East African Sunset Moth
Chrysiridia croesus
The wings of this East African species were used in Victorian costume jewelry.

White Apollo butterfly
Parnassius apollo
High-altitude meadows in European mountain ranges provide food for the larvae of this striking butterfly.

Brilliantly iridescent wings

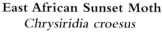

Red Admiral
Vanessa atalanta
Adults of this bright
species feed on flowers
and rotting fruit.

*Caterpillar eats
voraciously*

*Each hindwing has a
distinctive red spot*

Orange Sulfur
Colias eurytheme
Common in North America,
this is sometimes called the
"alfalfa" butterfly.

*Adult grows
inside a pupa,
attached to wood
or a leaf*

Life cycle
The life cycle of a butterfly is a series
of remarkable transformations. A
caterpillar emerges from the egg,
growing through a series of molts. The
adult emerges finally from the final
instar, or pupa (right).

Gulf Fritillary
Agraulis vanillae
This longwing species
lives in the southern
United States.

Menelaus Blue Morpho
Menelaus morpho
Iridescent turquoise above, the
undersides of the wings are
patterned like tree bark to
provide camouflage.

*Male flutters around
female during courtship*

BEETLES

About 450,000 species of beetles have been described; this is about 30 percent of all known animals. Estimates for the number of undiscovered beetles vary widely. Beetles have a hard exoskeleton and hard forewings (elytra), although not all species can fly. The life cycle involves four stages: egg, larva, pupa, and adult, or imago. Beetles are found in all natural habitats, including freshwater and marine environments, underground, and in dead and decaying vegetation.

Elytrum

True wing

Seven-spot Ladybug
Coccinella 7-punctata
In flight, it is possible to see the ladybug's true wings under the two hardened, red-and-black elytra.

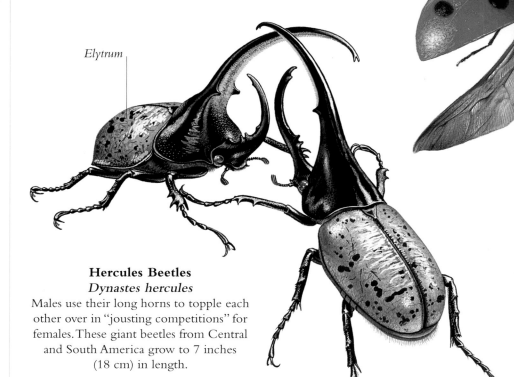

Elytrum

Hercules Beetles
Dynastes hercules
Males use their long horns to topple each other over in "jousting competitions" for females. These giant beetles from Central and South America grow to 7 inches (18 cm) in length.

Antler

African Fruit Beetle
Mecynorrhina polyphemus
These beetles use their antlers to release sap from tree bark; sap and fruit make up the majority of the adults' diet.

AN UNUSUAL LIFE CYCLE

Green Tiger Beetles lay their eggs in small burrows. When the eggs hatch, the larvae grab small spiders and ants that fall in. A parasitic wasp *Methoca ichneumonoides* also enters the burrow. Evading capture, it stings the tiger beetle larva and lays its own egg in the burrow—safe from predators. When the egg hatches, the wasp larva feeds on the body of the Green Tiger Beetle larva.

1. **Wingless parasitic wasp**, *Methoca ichneumonoides* attacking a predatory larva.
2. Larva of a **Green Tiger Beetle**, *Cicindela campestris,* in its burrow.

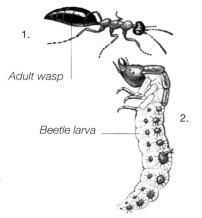

1.

Adult wasp

Beetle larva

2.

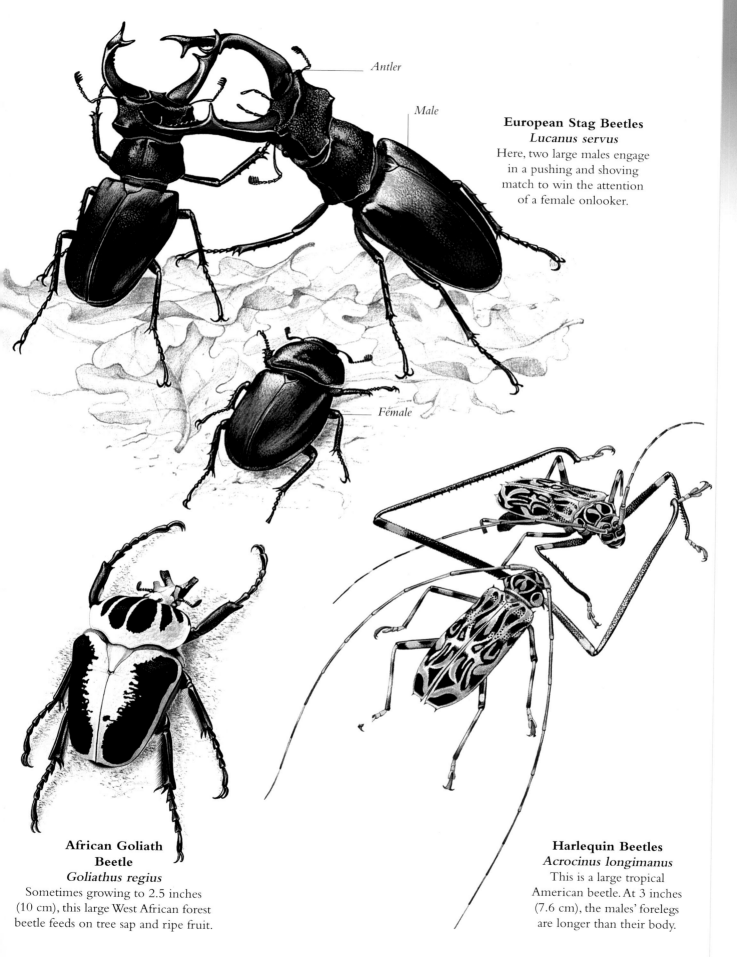

Antler

Male

European Stag Beetles
Lucanus servus
Here, two large males engage
in a pushing and shoving
match to win the attention
of a female onlooker.

Female

**African Goliath
Beetle**
Goliathus regius
Sometimes growing to 2.5 inches
(10 cm), this large West African forest
beetle feeds on tree sap and ripe fruit.

Harlequin Beetles
Acrocinus longimanus
This is a large tropical
American beetle. At 3 inches
(7.6 cm), the males' forelegs
are longer than their body.

SPIDERS

Spiders are predatory, carnivorous arthropods (order Araneae). Unlike insects, they have eight legs. More than 35,000 species have been described, and they play an important role in the balance of life by helping to control insect populations. They use venom for attack and defense, and employ silk for a variety of purposes, including web-building. Some are brightly colored, while others are inconspicuous or mimic insects.

Wasp Spider
Argiope bruennichi
Building a spiral orb web at dawn or dusk, this brightly colored spider immobilizes prey by wrapping it in silk, then injecting it with paralyzing venom and a protein-dissolving enzyme.

Wedding-present Spider
Pisaura mirabilis
Males of this species offer a nuptial gift—an item of prey wrapped in silk—to potential mates. The female bites on the gift and the male may then mate with her, keeping a leg on the gift.

SPIDER INTERNAL ANATOMY

Spiders' bodies are divided into two main sections, the cephalothorax (the combined head and thorax) and the abdomen. These two parts are joined by a narrow tube, the pedicel. The cephalothorax is covered by a hardened carapace and contains the brain, poison glands, and stomach. Six pairs of appendages grow from the cephalothorax: four pairs of legs, a pair of palps, and a pair of jaws (chelicerae) equipped with powerful fangs. There are no antennae, but the pedipalps act as feelers. The eyes are at the front of the cephalothorax. The visual acuity of most spiders is very poor. They are able to "listen" to the world around them through vibrations transmitted by air, the ground, their webs, or the surface of water. Below the eyes lie the chelicerae, a spider's offensive weapons. These can strike down like pickaxes or close together like tongs. Spiders feed by secreting or injecting digestive juices on to or into their prey, then sucking up the liquid food that results.

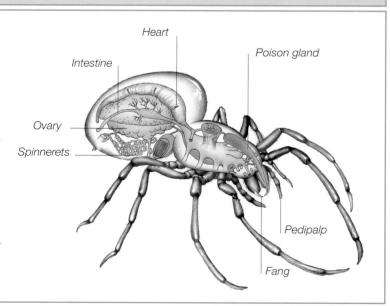

Heart

Poison gland

Intestine

Ovary

Spinnerets

Pedipalp

Fang

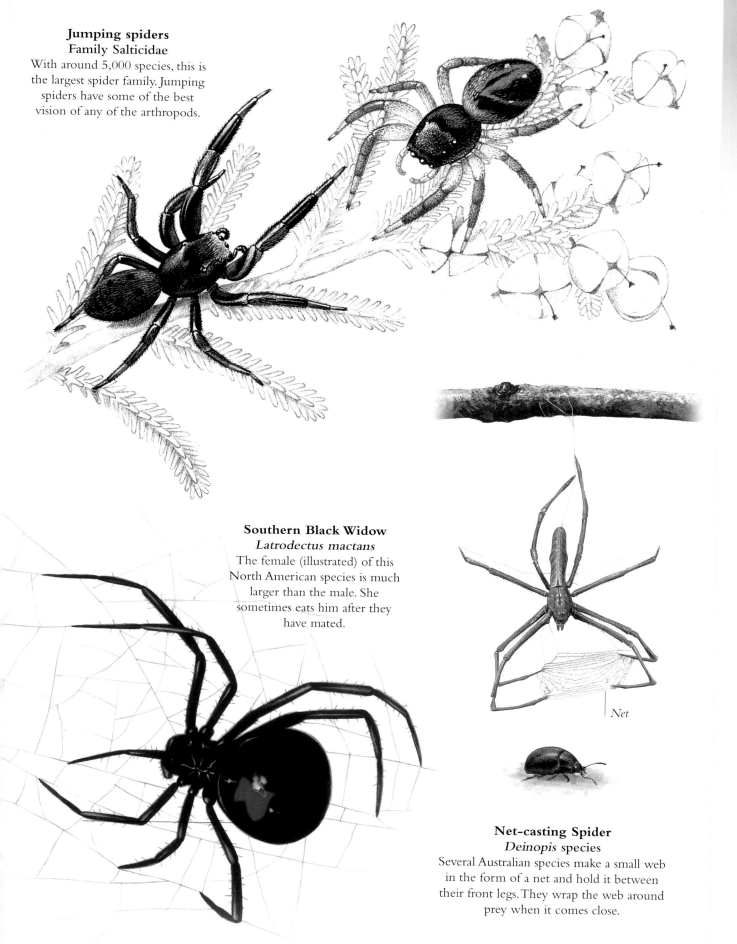

Jumping spiders
Family Salticidae
With around 5,000 species, this is the largest spider family. Jumping spiders have some of the best vision of any of the arthropods.

Southern Black Widow
Latrodectus mactans
The female (illustrated) of this North American species is much larger than the male. She sometimes eats him after they have mated.

Net

Net-casting Spider
Deinopis species
Several Australian species make a small web in the form of a net and hold it between their front legs. They wrap the web around prey when it comes close.

Windmill Books Ltd
First Floor
9-17 St. Albans Place
London N1 ONX
www.windmillbooks.co.uk

ISBN: 978-1-78121-131-1

Designers: Paul Drislane, Mike Davis
Design Manager: Keith Davis
Production: Richard Berry
Production Consultant: Alastair Gourlay
General Editor: Tim Harris
Editorial Director: Lindsey Lowe
Indexer: Ann Barrett

Printed in China